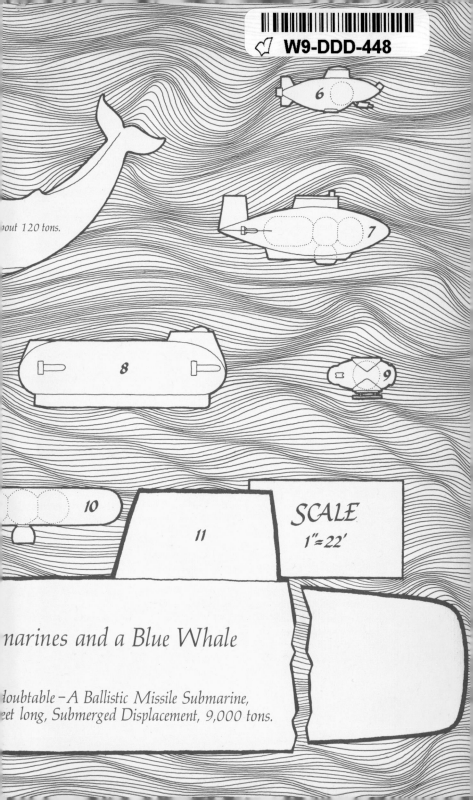

6

7

8

9

out 120 tons.

10

11

SCALE
1" ≈ 22'

narines and a Blue Whale

doubtable – A Ballistic Missile Submarine,
eet long, Submerged Displacement, 9,000 tons.

NOTES ON ENDPAPERS

1. *Trieste*—one of the first of the bathyscaphs, launched in Trieste in 1953 and purchased by the U.S. Office of Naval Research in 1958. Described even by its users as primarily an elevator, it nevertheless demonstrated that the entire ocean was open to exploration in free vehicles. The silhouette shown here is of the now-defunct *Trieste I* rather than of the improved second version, *Trieste II.*

2. The *Diving Saucer (La Soucoupe Plongeant)*—Cousteau's brilliant first exercise in the practicality of small-submarine operation. Launched in 1959, this tiny hull demonstrated that men could explore the seas at a cost that even private organizations could afford.

3. *Alvin*—the first all-American entry into the research-submarine field. Funded by the U.S. Navy and operated by Woods Hole Oceanographic Institution, it has a 6,500-foot limit and has already repaid many times over its initial cost of less than $1 million.

4. *Aluminaut*—an innovation in hull materials. One of its key architects was Dr. Edward Wenk, later chairman of the National Council on Marine Resources and Engineering Development.

5. *Yomiuri*—one of the first of the Japanese research submarines, was financed by a newspaper. With a depth limit of about 2,000 feet, it is of moderate performance but an indication that many nations have the will and the ability to play a role in the deep seas.

6. *Deep Star III*—one of an increasing number of small submarines built entirely by private funds, in this case General Dynamics/Electric Boat, a yard that has pioneered in military-submarine design for more than half a century. This is a second-generation design with emphasis on its capability as a work boat.

7. *Deep Quest*—a second-generation craft designed by Lockheed. The hull is of an exotic steel alloy and the depth performance exceeds 8,000 feet. A lock-in lock-out chamber for divers is provided.

8. PX *15*—the *Benjamin Franklin*, Piccard-Grumman design. It is a relatively large, non-nuclear submarine built for long endurance and a large crew and has many innovations (for submarines) in the life support system.

9. DOWB—a General Motors entry. Small, deep-diving (6,500 feet), work-rather than research-oriented, this has unusual viewing optics.

10. DSRV (Deep Submergence Rescue Vehicle)—the first "production" submarine. Being built by the U.S. Navy to provide superior rescue capability for military submarines in trouble; and to double when available as a survey, exploration, and research craft.

11. *Le Redoubtable*, prototype of the submarine by which France hopes to establish a creditable ocean-based nuclear threat. In cost and tonnage, one nuclear attack submarine of the type being built by the score in Russia and the United States, and in smaller numbers by other countries, outweighs all the research and work submarines (excluding the nuclear NR *1*) that have been built to date. However, a nuclear military submarine must be self-sufficient for months. Were the cost and tonnage of the support ships required by the nonmilitary submarines also thrown into the balance, the comparison would be less overpowering.

The Realm of the Submarine

The Realm of th

SUBMARINE

BY *Paul Cohen*

The Macmillan Company
Collier-Macmillan Ltd., *London*

72994

Library of Congress Catalog Card Number: 69-12176

FIRST PRINTING

The Macmillan Company
Collier-Macmillan Canada Ltd., Toronto, Ontario

Printed in the United States of America

To Ruth for her counsel and patience

Acknowledgments

Many friends have been kind enough to interrupt their busy lives to read one or another chapter in this book. As best they could, they have tactfully tried to guide the author's headlong dive into the mighty ocean of fact and opinion that is current submarine technology. If they have not always succeeded, it is because of the author's inability to comprehend in true proportion all of the factors that are shaping this dynamic field.

In particular, the author wishes to thank Rear Admiral M. H. Rindskopf, Captain A. F. Kennedy, Captain Howard Bucknell, Capt. Frank C. Fogarty and Cdr. Malcom Mac-Kinnon of the U.S. Navy for their comments on the chapter on military submarines; Dr. Herman E. Sheets, vice president for research and engineering, General Dynamics/Electric Boat, for his views on the cargo submarine; Mr. R. R. Loughman of General Dynamics/Electric Boat for his insider's knowledge of the design problems associated with the research and work submarine; Mr. K. Arnold and Mr. R. D. Hawkins for aid with the chapter on Underwater Structures; Mr. Andre Galerne, president, International Underwater Contractors, Inc., whose lifetime of experience with professional diving helped to correct some inferences in the chapter on divers; and Dr. Frank Andrews, who, as Captain Andrews, USN, held a major position in the search for the *Thresher,* for his corrections to my account of that precedent-making deep-water effort.

By conversation and letters, many others have helped to shape this book. I regret that I cannot in every case make a specific acknowledgment.

For errors of fact and judgment the author alone is responsible.

Paul Cohen

Contents

Foreword

THE CENTRAL PROBLEM this world faces for the rest of the twentieth century is neither war nor peace, but the need to maintain a population still growing unchecked. Man, the climax predator who preys on every species that meets his fancy and on whom no animal dares feed, is the victim of his biological success. Dominant on this planet, he scours its surface in such numbers that, worldwide, malnutrition is his most serious disease. No longer content with taking the living, he must dig into the earth for the fuels and minerals that were laid down in the past.

Under the most conservative predictions, more of those raw materials that feed an industrialized society will be needed in the last third of this century than have been used since men became metallurgists some 6,000 to 7,000 years ago. Why not, when more than ten times as many people use fuels and metals scores of times faster than in the distant past. The richest and most accessible ore deposits on land have long since been stripped. It took centuries to clear the Persian rivers of gold. It took only decades to exhaust those of Alaska. The tin ores of Cornwall, which ancient men considered inexhaustible, vanished quickly with the coming of the industrial revolution. Later and larger examples will soon disfigure every continent. To the extent that it becomes economically feasible, the world has no choice but to turn to the treasures still hidden in the deeps.

In this domain man's principal tools are the submarine, the diver, and a variety of ocean platforms. Under the lash of his relentless ingenuity these devices are developing faster than the world can learn how to deal with the economic and political pressures they are generating. Now that the gleam of wealth can be perceived in the blackness of the abyss, territorial hackles are beginning to arise. For the world's continental shelves, an area as large as Africa, some tenuous precedents of ownership exist. But the deep ocean bottoms, which in the foreseeable future can be reached only by the prodigious expenditure of money and technology, are owned by nobody. Only a high level of statesmanship can prevent the international jockeying already underway from becoming one more long struggle for possession of a new world.

This book is about the technology that separates the haves from the have-nots in this world of cold and pressure, a world whose *Santa Marias* are submarines. Although military submarines have been used in large numbers (but only near the surface) for more than half a century, the era with which this book will be principally concerned dates from 1948, when the slow, clumsy, and now obsolescent bathyscaph demonstrated that man could descend into the deepest wrinkles on this planet's crust.

In the following chapters the major developments in submarine and diving technology that are at the base of our newfound ability to work in the oceans will be examined, as will the factors that permit commercial organizations and institutions of learning to build and own their own submarines or individuals to buy "build-it-yourself" kits from magazine advertisements. The network of needs that connect divers and submarines will be looked at, as will the complex feedback that exists between military necessity, oceanography, research submarines, and the exploitation of the undersea world.

Plato, who based his opinions on the writings of Solon some centuries earlier, who in turn (probably incorrectly) translated some still earlier Egyptian texts, believed that a huge island had existed just west of the Pillars of Hercules, that it housed a rich and powerful kingdom, and that it had vanished in a cataclysmic catastrophe some ten or twelve millennia before Christ. This was Atlantis, mother of legend.

Whatever the basis for this myth, there does exist a true Atlantis, the kingdom of the sea. The oceans that cover almost three-quarters of this globe hide within them the food, the minerals, and the space that can hold back—at least for a while—the Malthusian demons that haunt so much of this world.

The World Beneath the Sea

The nation that first learns how to live under the seas will control them, and the nation that controls the seas will control the world.
—G. V. Petrovich, *Soviet scientist*

Horatio, Lord Nelson put it more succinctly. "Who rules the seas, rules the world." Nor did he have in mind just his men-of-war. From his day-to-day experience, he knew that the oceans were the world's common highway, the route that connected every major country with every other and (as it remains) the most efficient means of heavy transport. It was the economic power of British merchant fleets rather than the fire power of Nelson's men-of-war that was the first and broadest buttress of the empire.

Today, in a world inhabited by five times the population of Nelson's day, the role of the ocean in maintaining some semblance of comfort and security in human life has become complex almost beyond comprehension. Although planes weighing more than 350 tons are now flying (heavier than most of the merchant men that Nelson guarded), ships still carry more than 99 percent of all cargo that moves between continents. Oil tankers and ore carriers two, three, and even four times the size of the *Queen Mary* are now afloat. A minor interference with this traffic, such as seems to occur every decade or so, raises the threat of starvation and in-

dustrial stagnation to many nations. England faced a crisis
because of the interruption of her oil supply when the plans
of France and Great Britain to take the Suez Canal in the
mid-1950s were aborted. In 1967 when the war between
Israel and the Arab states again closed the canal, the chain
of food ships to India was temporarily interrupted, and several states in that subcontinent went on short rations.

Fishing output has grown prodigiously—the only major
source of food that continues to increase faster than, and in
some recent years several times faster than, the world's population. For many nations, the sea offers the only practical
source of sufficient protein. In the United States, however, a
nation so sated with abundance that even dog foods are advertised as low-calorie, the fish catch has in recent years
shown no steady upward trend. It still lands several million
tons a year, which statistically gives the United States a per
capita consumption of fish twice that of the world as a
whole. Actually, most of the catch is eaten by livestock,
poultry, and household pets.

In another area, however, the United States must turn to
the sea in dead earnest. Once a great exporter of raw materials, the United States is now one of the have-not nations
and depends for her industrial productivity on increasing
and massive imports of petroleum, iron ore, and many other
strategic materials. It is an economic trend of dead certainty
that the United States will become more dependent on sea-
borne imports and on materials from the ocean floor as the
decades roll on.

Although the oceans have as yet been subjected to only
the sketchiest of surveys, with the most inadequate of equipment, it is already apparent that it contains enormous quantities of oil and many other valuable minerals. Before these

can be brought to the refineries and smelters they must run a hurdle of geopolitical, oceanographic, engineering, and economic barriers. To those who solve this conundrum—which of the minerals in which of the deposits can win this obstacle race—will go some of the richest economic prizes of the century.

The oceans have been exploited for food and transport, and to some degree for minerals and living space, for millennia. The new ingredient is technology. After a century of growth, oceanography has become a mature science that, together with a multitude of terrestrial technologies, has created the new field of underwater engineering. The chief tools of this new discipline are free divers using relatively simple equipment, saturated divers using complex and costly paraphernalia, and an almost bewildering variety of small, versatile submarines. Thus equipped, armies of engineers and scientists are turning their attention to the more than two-thirds of this planet that is covered with salt water.

The extent of this development can be grasped by looking at the situation at the beginning of World War II and comparing it with the present. In the late 1930s oceanography was a well-defined but little-known field of science with about a century of history. It had a core of dedicated scientists, perhaps a few hundred throughout the world. Their facilities were a handful of institutions and an assortment of small ships, most of them powered by sail.

The submarine was an auxiliary naval vessel—a proven and deadly harasser of surface ships, but not in the main line of battle. The ocean surfaces were thought to be controlled by the heavily armored capital ships, and who cared about the depths? Submarines were either scouts or instruments of guerrilla action by have-not nations.

Amateur divers were essentially nonexistent, and the world of professional divers numbered perhaps a few hundred. They wore cumbersome "hard-hat" suits, were tied to a surface tender and crew by an airline, and rarely went deeper than 200 feet. Devices for "free" diving, in which the diver carried his breathing supply on his back, were in existence but were either limited in endurance or dangerous. Although self-contained equipment was the choice of divers on military missions, very few commercial or professional divers used it. The retired diver could almost invariably be picked out by eye—crippled and deformed from repeated bouts of the "bends."

Fishing practices had been only sketchily affected by the technological revolution that had occurred on land. The nets and trawls themselves were evolving with almost glacial slowness, and the major technical innovations on fishing vessels were the diesel engine and powered winches.

Salvage was a chancy business, a more certain way even than gold mining for shiny-eyed adventurers to go broke. Undersea mining was so rare as to be virtually unknown. Above all, there was no sense of excitement or urgency and no general awareness of what was hidden below the surfaces of the oceans.

As we approach this century's eighth decade, we stand just inside the gate to this underwater world. We cannot see very far; only about 10 percent of the ocean bottom has been mapped in any significant detail, and practically none of it, in a statistical sense, has been carefully prospected. Important deposits of minerals are now known to rest on the bottom, from gold- and platinum-bearing sands that line part of the Alaskan coastline to continuous blankets of manganese that cover thousands of square miles of deep water. New areas for fisheries continue to be discovered. Billions of dollars are being invested in ocean-based industries. Yet overall, data on resources are scanty, and we sense rather than know the potential.

The atomic submarine, carrying atomic missiles, has become the new queen of battle. Driven first by the need to learn everything about the oceans that will increase the effectiveness of the submarine, or will enable it to be hunted down, and now also by the hope of economic gain, the maritime powers are supporting oceanography lavishly. Suddenly, after a century of obscurity, it is a glamour science. Nations compete in the size of their fleets of oceanographic vessels. Some of these ships have become almost uncomfortably large and pretentious for the older oceanographers, who grew up in an era where aceticism in equipment and stoicism to personal discomfort was the only possible way of life.

Submarine technology has advanced so far that small nonmilitary submarines have become practical devices for research institutions and private companies. Their number is increasing so fast that no publication with as long a reaction time as a book dare print a list of those already in operation. It would be out of date in a month. And these small submersibles, many built with private funds, frequently go to depths that no military submarine has ever reached. In 1963 when the *Thresher* went down in 8,500 feet of water, the United States could marshal only one vehicle, the *Trieste I*, to put men close to the bottom so that they could search with their own eyes. In 1966 when a twenty-megaton nuclear bomb fell into the sea off Spain, several submersibles were in action within days, and the bomb, a very small needle in a very large haystack, was recovered.

Although there has been a great decline in the position of

the capital ship, with the battleship all but vanished, the heavy cruiser obsolete, and the value of the carrier in any but policing operations increasingly questioned, merchant ships are prospering. Oil tankers have now become the largest ships that have ever existed. Scores of them can lift more than 100,000 tons of oil; some can lift over 300,000 tons. Submarines have grown much larger too, but the largest of them are quite small compared to the bulk carriers. Nevertheless, interest in submarine cargo vessels continues to persist. One reason is that American and Russian submarines are traversing the Arctic Ocean, under the ice, with increasing frequency.

Millions of free divers (well over a million in the United States alone) now work and play in rivers, in lakes, and on the continental shelves. They bring up Spanish treasure in Florida, repair intake gates at the bottom of deep reservoirs, study seals in the Antarctic, clear blocked aqueducts in Chicago, investigate the cause of ship sinkings for the Coast Guard, and conduct sabotage in Vietnam. Not content with diving until their air supply is exhausted and then coming to the surface for decompression, they are learning how to live in underwater houses for weeks at a time and at depths that would have seemed ludicrous even to Jules Verne. By staying down for long periods, active and in good health, they are improving the effectiveness and output of divers by scores of time. Underwater tasks of a scope, depth, and complexity not envisioned even five years ago are now economic.

As for fishing, the total world catch has increased about fourfold in thirty years, and the rate of increase continues at 6 to 8 percent per year. Most of this increase, however, has come about by the opening of new areas to fishing, such as the enormously productive grounds off Peru. Overall, the fish species living close to the surface and many on the shallow bottoms are fairly heavily exploited. Attention is therefore turning to the middle depths and to the deeper bottoms. In Japan and Russia, and to some extent in the United States, the submarine has been pressed into service as an ideal vehicle with which to explore for new sources of supply and to conduct fisheries research. The world's fishing fleets —many of them to a greater extent than the United States' —are making use of sophisticated vessels and of oceanographic instrumentation: sonar and temperature data for locating schools of fish, fathometers for telling the crew something about the depth and nature of the bottom or how deep the fish are, Loran and other navigation devices to tell them precisely where they are, radio communications, a variety of improved nets and trawls, even electronic lures. Large sonars on the ocean floor near England and the Hawaiian Islands have been used to locate schools of fish, the data on their location then being radiotelephoned to nearby fishing vessels. One result of such progress is visible in the whaling industry, where specialized equipment has worked so well that many of the large whale species are now close to extinction. It is inevitable that developments in fishing equipment now underway will force the world's fishing fleets to exercise restraint on an international scale if they are not to exterminate species much smaller and more numerous than whales.

The exploitation of underwater deposits of oil and gas has become the major area of expansion in the petroleum industry. Oil or gas in production quantities has been found in the Persian Gulf, off Nigeria, off Australia, off the East Indies, off Alaska, in the Gulf of Mexico, in the North Sea—in short, off every continent and many large islands.

Diamonds are being mined off southwest Africa. The largest sulfur mine in the world lies seven miles off Louisiana. Tin has been dredged for years from the rivers and shallow bays off Malaysia and Indonesia.

These are some of the trends. To understand where they may lead requires at least a basic understanding of the tools of undersea exploration and their capabilities and limitations.

First, with the searches for the USS *Thresher* and for the H-bomb lost off Spain as case histories, this book will examine the difficulties of probing at the bottom from the distant surface. Then some of the new forms of submarines currently evolving will be described. Because of the complex partnership that is being created between divers and submarines, the problems of the modern diver will also be looked at; for in a strong sense the diver, with his communication equipment, life support systems, and undersea habitats, is becoming increasingly a miniaturized submersible. Finally, with trepidation, some predictions will be made about the future of man in the sea.

Looking at the Bottom
from the Top

You can't push with a rope.
—Sailor's adage

THE FIRST OBJECT ever brought back by the hand of man from the deep ocean—and it took almost five months of desperate work to retrieve it—was a piece of copper pipe, part of the debris torn off the United States submarine *Thresher* as it plunged to its grave on April 10, 1963. In a way it wasn't even the hand of man that grasped this twisted artifact but rather a barely operable iron claw—a manipulator—bolted to the underside of the bathyscaph *Trieste*. Except for a few pieces of wreckage dredged up by surface trawls, that is all that was ever recovered from the wreck.

Three years later, when a crash between an American bomber and a refueling plane dropped a 20-megaton H-bomb into the Mediterranean, the United States Navy was able to recover it intact from 2,900 feet of water. It took almost 80 days, during which the bomb was found, lost, and found again. But three years of rapid development had given the Navy some new tools, and the bomb came up.

Four years later (August 10, 1967) the Navy sunk an old liberty ship, the *Robert Louis Stevenson,* off the Aleutian

Islands. It was rigged to sink quickly and explode as part of an experiment in monitoring large explosions. The ship refused to either sink or explode but instead drifted for twenty hours, hidden from sight. Its final resting place and condition were determined in a few weeks of search, using by now routine instruments and methods.

When the *Thresher* went down in the Gulf of Maine, the only vehicle owned by the United States that could search at the required depth—8,400 feet—was the *Trieste,* then in San Diego. It made its first dive off New England on June 24, two and a half months later. In the case of the hydrogen bomb off Spain, the United States had assembled, within days, an armada of four submarines, twenty-five U.S. Navy surface ships, four commercial ships, and over 3,000 men.

Although the hunt for the H-bomb was the largest and most intensive underwater search ever undertaken and the two year hunt for the remains of the *Thresher* was the second largest such search, this is not their significant aspect. Each crisis marshaled every applicable resource, regardless of expense, that the richest and most technically developed nation on earth could provide. The equipment made available off Palomares, Spain, however, was decisively better in quality and quantity than what, three years earlier, could be put into the Gulf of Maine. Not that the abyss has been conquered. The location of the *Thresher* and of the hydrogen bomb were known within a few miles, in one case by the presence of a support ship accompanying the *Thresher* and in the other by the presence of a sharp-eyed and quick-witted Spanish fisherman. However, when the USS *Scorpion* went down about May 21, 1968, no such accurate estimate of its location was available. An area of doubt measured in scores of miles rather than in miles, explains why months of search were required to produce hard evidence on the location of the wreck.

When the SSN 593, the USS *Thresher*, with 129 men aboard, failed to surface from a test dive, an immense hunt was immediately mounted. The *Atlantis II*, queen of American oceanographic ships and fresh from its builder's trials, was diverted from its first scheduled voyage to the Indian Ocean. Nor was that the only oceanographic expedition delayed that year. Detection devices still in the development stage were brought into action, and special instrumentation was improvised. Because the existing navigation techniques for the area were far too imprecise for a bottom search, new radio navigation systems were set up and special maps were prepared. Eventually the tiny area that was thought to contain the wreckage, roughly ten nautical miles on a side, became the best-mapped section of ocean-covered earth on this planet. To make it so required the dedicated labors of scores of highly skilled professionals, working for the better part of two years with tools that were, in an absolute sense, generally inadequate.

Because months were required to bring *Trieste* onto the scene and it was pointless to send down this delicate, ponderous, and slow-moving vessel (a man could walk three times faster than its top speed) until the wreckage area was pinpointed, the search first employed surface vehicles.

These were floating a mile and a half above the wreckage. An initial two-week survey disclosed about one hundred "contacts" that might have been the *Thresher*. As was learned after the fact, one of the indications recorded within a few hours after the search was started and for a while thought to be the wreck was a sharp change in the geological structure of the bottom. The charts soon became studded with other anomalies that also could have been the submarine.

The ultra-precision fathometers (depth sounders) on the oceanographic ships soon indicated that about half the area was studded with rock out-crops, ridges, and large boulders, and was far too rough to permit the detection of an object as small as a submarine by sonar. (The terrain into which the H-bomb dropped was even rougher.)

The indications of the various instruments on the ships had to be matched with photographic or visual confirmation. That could be done only if the distance between instruments and wreckage were shortened to feet instead of miles. Eventually, a trail of debris half a mile wide and at least two miles long was charted, and more than 100,000 photographs taken of the bottom in the vicinity of the *Thresher* sinking. Although, during the second summer of search, the *Trieste II* sat for over an hour on the sand-covered remains of part of the engine room, most of the photographs taken were of the conning tower, tail structure, bow domes, and other auxiliary portions of the hull and some debris from the interior of the submarine. The main pressure hull is buried in the bottom.

One can only speculate on how *Thresher* met its end. If the Navy panel that investigated the disaster is correct, the initial cause of the sinking most probably was a failure in the nightmare maze of piping that fills the interior of a military submarine. Were the break in the salt-water piping, the ship would have started to fill rather slowly. (The word "slowly" is used relative to the great internal volume of the hull.) It could well be that high-pressure jets of salt water were already beyond the capability of the submarine's tank-blowing capacity, or that the inrushing water compounded the problem by shorting out electrical power lines or by creating a condition that caused the reactor to shut down. If it were deprived of power, the submarine would not be able to muster all the reserves of buoyancy that it might otherwise have had. As the submarine sank deeper (and it was already near test depth), it quickly reached its crushing depth; for submarines are built, like airplanes, with a very small factor of safety. Once the main hull crushed, overwhelming quantities of water crashed in quickly, killing the crew and filling the entire structure except for a few air pockets where the highly compressed (and therefore heavy) air was of little use in slowing the descent. The savage vibrations that resulted as the hull crushed were probably responsible for shaking off the debris later found on the bottom. The submarine—all 3,000 tons of it—now picked up speed, probably, and started to fall some 6,000 or 7,000 feet to the bottom. It had been a highly streamlined object, with huge stabilizing fins that would keep it pointed nose down. But stripped of the light, free flooding structure that give the blunt pressure hull of a submarine its streamlined shape, it may have tumbled as it fell. Bow fairings, conning tower, stabilizers fluttered behind it; lead ballast, cables, battery plates spilled out of the ruptured hull to form the long junkyard that is the only tombstone of this vessel. A photograph exists of a twelve-foot compressed-air cylinder torn loose from the *Thresher* that hit the bottom hard enough to bury five feet of itself in the silt and clay.

The first approach of the search vessels was to lower a variety of devices that included still cameras,* television cameras, magnetometers, and high-resolution sonars on the

---

* Photographic equipment to observe the deep ocean bottom had been built up over the years primarily at the urging of submarine geologists; in a similar evolution, the magnetic detection gear (MAD) used by airplanes to detect submarines in World War II had its genesis in the search by oil geologists for magnetic anomalies in the earth.

end of long cables. The searchers did this of necessity, not choice, for they were aware, as most laymen are not, of the frustrating and peculiar problems that affect an oceanographer when he tries to move an instrument precisely at the end of a very long and twisting line. The problem can be difficult if all he wants to do is to sample the ocean at some selected depth and he doesn't care whether the sample is from part of the ocean a quarter mile to one side of his ship or the other. To locate a particular point in the ocean with a long line—let alone to find it once and then come back to it later—becomes virtually impossible. It's like probing in the dark for a very small object with an extraordinary long and limber stick.

Cables sway in the unknown underwater currents of the ocean like lines of a spider's cobweb in a breeze. So do, in fact, columns of steel oil-well casing if they are long enough. One would think that a heavy steel pipe a foot in diameter and with walls half an inch thick would stay fairly well in line. And it does if it is short. But when the pipe gets to be two or three miles long, some very unusual undulations can appear. The problem is by no means theoretical. Cores are already being drilled in bottoms miles below the surface.

A line can stream out astern, then—deep out of sight— swing off in an unexpected direction. As has been found in the past ten years, deep-sea currents are far more rapid and variable in direction than oceanographers had supposed. Nor does it help, if a precise position of an instrument package is desired, that the surface ship is frequently drifting relative to the bottom under the influence of shifting winds and currents. The situation is improving with modern radio-navigation techniques like Loran and Decca, helped by inertial navigational equipment and satellite fixes, the position of a surface ship can be known to a rather high degree of accuracy—as little as a few hundred feet error. The submarine does not have so many alternatives—radio transmission underwater is essentially impossible.

With acoustic techniques there are ways, by no means simple, of measuring the position of the instrument package relative to the ship. In one case off Bermuda, a surface ship was moving in one direction and its instrument package —20,000 feet down—was moving in the other direction for almost half an hour.

In the days when metals could not achieve their current tensile strengths, steel cables could break of their own weight if great lengths were payed out. Therefore tapered cables have been resorted to, with the end deep in the water thinner and less heavy per running foot than the section near the ship, which must take the greatest strain. Lines of synthetic plastics like nylon, which is very strong for its weight and almost buoyant (in fact, neutrally buoyant cables are available), have cured the problem of breakage due to the cable's weight. They have not cured the problems of breakage per se.

If the seas get rough and the surface ship starts to pitch and heave,* the drag and inertia of the cable (the load at the end of it is rarely a significant factor) can so firmly resist a sudden upward motion of the ship that cables snap with factors of safety that would be considered unnecessarily high in land-based applications.

This is not to decry cables, which will continue to be used—and with good economic reason—when the ship can heave to or moves only slowly and when the particular part

---

* A ship has six degrees of freedom, or motion. Three are rotations; three are translations, or movements along a line. The rotations are, respectively, pitch, roll, and yaw, which even the casual sailor can identify; the translations along the corresponding axes are sway, surge, and heave.

of the bottom that is scraped or viewed, or that part of the ocean that is sampled doesn't matter. For such applications cables are the cheapest, simplest, most reliable means for getting instrument packages deep into the oceans. As oceanographic investigations increase so, in an absolute sense, will cable lowerings. But they are no longer the only way.

Since radio navigation is not available to a deeply submerged submarine, recourse was had, during the *Thresher* search, to the "fortune cooky" technique. These "fortune cookies" were plastic sheets, about 16 by 22 inches, numbered consecutively. Each was rolled up, tied with a band that later dissolved in salt water, and weighted with an ordinary sash weight. They were dropped overboard at approximately seventy-five-foot intervals from ships that ran as true to evenly spaced straight lines as they could. Since the "fortune cookies" took about an hour to sink to the bottom, the grid below was not perfect, but it proved of great value in telling *Trieste* not only where it was but if, in a later dive, it was returning to a desired point.

It is noteworthy that three years later, off Palomares, Spain, the *Alvin* and the *Aluminaut* (on which the main burden of search had fallen) had at least as great a problem in returning to the same spot in a later dive as did *Trieste*. Nor did the rough bottom off Palomares lend itself to the use of "fortune cookies."

The bomb had fallen on January 17, 1966, from the wreckage of a B-52 bomber after it had collided with a KC-135 jet-refueling tanker. On February 1, the 11-ton *Alvin*, partially dismantled, was loaded on a C-133 transport from Woods Hole, Massachusetts, to Spain. After two test dives, the *Alvin* began its search on February 14. She was one of four submersibles eventually on the scene. The others were the *Deep Jeep,* developed by the Naval Ordnance Test Station at China Lake, California, and capable of working to about 2,000 feet; a Cubmarine sub of relatively shallow capability; and the fifty-one-foot *Aluminaut,* built for the Reynolds Aluminum Company, and at the time the biggest and deepest-diving research submarine in the United States.

The search was conducted in an area already "pinpointed" by a Spanish fisherman. He had taken several bearings on peaks he could recognize on shore, a method as old as sailing. It proved in the end to be remarkably accurate—a true "pinpoint." But this the Navy did not know. The area that was searched intensively was several square miles in extent. (That is still a "pinpoint" in the ocean and gave the searchers a big advantage over the ships that began the *Thresher* hunt.)

Visibility near the bottom under the submarine's floodlights varied from about 20 to 30 feet (rather good) to near zero when storms came up. The terrain was even worse than that in which *Thresher* went down: rough, with sharp inclines and cut up by ravines with slopes to 70 degrees—real precipices. Half a month later, on March 1, *Alvin* found the track of the bomb, a deep furrow in the mud. But because it could not maneuver quickly enough, it overshot the track. Because of the rough terrain and the low visibility, *Alvin* searched for five hours more and could not even relocate the track. It is a vital point that *Alvin* did not search the area "systematically." Rather, the pilot reasoned that the bomb probably slid down one of the narrow ravines. Therefore, if he ran along the rims of the canyons looking for the bomb's tracks he would save time. Had he searched along some computerized grid, the search would have taken longer.

Some twelve days later *Alvin* found the track again, fol-

lowed it, and lost it. On the next day *Alvin* finally found the
cylinder and its parachute, in 2,500 feet of water, lying in a
crevasse. *Aluminaut* was immediately called in to help the
surface ships above in placing the bomb's location on their
maps. Both submarines then settled down to keep watch.
The *Alvin,* with its lesser endurance, had to return to the
surface eight hours later. The larger *Aluminaut* baby-sat
with the bomb for an additional 14 hours.

The next day *Alvin* took down a three-eighths-inch line
and attempted to anchor it in the soft bottom, without success. (Small submarines, like divers, can push or pull with
surprisingly little force.) A heavier line was sent down, but
its anchor pulled loose. Then the weather turned bad.

Work was resumed on March 18 in fairly rough seas. The
surface ship, attempting to lower a camera on a line, had to
give up the attempt. *Alvin* tried to grab the bomb in a large
claw attached to its manipulator and failed. Again weather
intervened. Work began topside on an improvised recovery
device.

On March 23 the six-by-six-foot recovery frame and its
grappling hooks were dropped within seventy feet of the
bomb—remarkable precision. Then in a series of frustrating
maneuvers, *Alvin* tried, with its manipulator, to entangle the
grappling hooks in the lines of the parachute. The lines
swayed in the bottom currents, eluding every attempt of the
experienced pilots to grasp them in the manipulator. The
problem was simply beyond the capabilities of the existing
equipment and the maneuverability of the eleven-ton *Alvin.*
Finally, in desperation, the pilots picked up a grappling
hook attached to the anchor line and entangled it in the
shrouds. The next day the surface ship attempted to lift the
bomb. *Alvin* was on the scene, but for reasons that no one

saw or understood the line broke and the bomb slipped down the slope into the darkness and was lost again.

That was March 24. It took nine days of searching to find it again, 300 feet below its previous location. As soon as possible, *Aluminaut* was called in and baby-sat over the bomb for 22 hours while the exhausted crew and the exhausted batteries of *Alvin* repaired to the surface.

By that time a contraption called CURV, an unmanned device developed by the Naval Ordnance Test Station at Pasadena to recover torpedoes in deep water, was on the scene. It is unmanned only by definition. A five-man crew aboard a surface ship was required to operate it. Bad weather again intervened. After several tense incidents, CURV was sent down, became entangled in the lines of the now-billowing chute, and made an inelegant but successful recovery of the bomb, almost eighty days after the crash that dropped it into the Mediterranean. Actually CURV dragged the bomb to within 200 feet of the surface, where frogmen, unable to work on the deep bottom, secured lines around the cylinder and pulled it to the surface.

It was an operation that was just within the capability of the existing equipment and the extraordinary skillful, resourceful, and dedicated men that manned the equipment. To apply economic standards to such an event is irrelevant and impractical. The recovery of a twenty-megaton hydrogen bomb—of a power so cataclysmic that it can only be described by abstract numbers—was vital for reason piled on reason— technical, moral, legal, or plain fear that it would fall into someone else's hands.

With the profoundest respect to the high professionalism of the men who recovered the H-bomb, it must still be said that the available equipment was not yet well matched to the difficulties of deep-sea operations. If routine salvage operations are to be attempted, or if the profitable exploitation of the many already known mineral deposits in deep water is to be undertaken, the job must be done by ordinary individuals, under no undue stress, in relative comfort and safety, motivated only by the usual desires to earn their salaries and do their job. That situation is coming about.

Let us look approximately a decade into the future. A huge dredge, or rather a marine mining plant, lies in the Gulf Stream. Although the dredge lies unanchored in one of the swiftest regions of the stream, it hangs virtually motionless in the choppy current. The answer is to be found in four big propellers at the corners of the dredge, responding automatically to the orders of a computer that is fed with data from a trio of hydrophones on the underside of the hull. On the ocean bottom, far below, is a carefully surveyed grid of sonic pingers, the references above which the dredge sits regardless of wind, weather, and current.

Alongside the dredge is tied an ore carrier, with black streams of ore pouring into its open hatches. From the fifty-foot-high A-frame at the head of the dredge dangles a heavy, semiflexible tube, two feet in diameter. One end disappears into the water. The other end enters the huge superstructure of the dredge, from which emanates the steady roar of pumps and the ore-processing mills. As the barge rolls and pitches in the swell, the A-frame swings to compensate, so that the pipe, where it enters the water, scarcely moves.

The dredge is anchored over the Blake Plateau, just north of the Bahamas. It is an easily accessible area under extensive exploration since 1956. In 1965 it was discovered that the northern end of this plateau is paved continuously with manganese dioxide over an area of about 2,000 square miles. Nor is that the end of manganese and phosphate deposits on the plateau.

This pavement lies primarily between latitudes 31°00′ and 32°10′, that is, opposite the coast of Georgia, beyond the continental shelf, and about 150 to 250 miles offshore. The water is only modestly deep. At its shallowest, the pavement lies below 1,200 feet of water; at its deepest, below 2,500 feet—reasonably shallow, considering that the average depth of the ocean is almost 15,000 feet.

The pavement is not very thick, on the average about three inches, but its vast extent makes it a very large deposit indeed. Nor is it solid manganese oxide. It is layered with phosphate and calcite sediment and occasionally carries traces of copper and cobalt, metals worth more on a per pound basis than the manganese.

The thirty men on the dredge are not much in evidence, for most of the activity is occurring in the processing room. There a slurry of water and ore rattling up from the ocean bottom is crushed, conveyed over vibrating screens, freed of as much dross as possible, and dried before tumbling down the chute into the ore ship. The scene is not much different from that in a metal-refining plant on shore except for the slight motion of the ship. As in an automated land-based ore-processing plant of the period, it is highly automated. The few men in evidence are sitting relaxed behind a series of consoles in an air-conditioned control room just aft of the bridge.

The really unusual activity is occurring far below the surface, on the hard, smooth pavement 1,500 feet below the dredge. There a one-hundred-foot submarine, eighteen feet in diameter, with two long skids on its underside, lies horizontally on the hard black pavement. It is aligned almost due north and south, its nose pointing into the current, the only visible evidence of which are the bending of the few sea fans that manage to find a foothold on this almost sterile bottom. The bow of the submarine is a hemisphere of transparent glass. Inside the sphere two men sit in sport shirts and slippered feet watching a trawl whose long treads make it look like an armored tank. The two men in the control cockpit are down only for an eight-hour shift. They do not need a galley, a stall shower, an elaborate life support system, and the maintenance staff required by a military submarine that must remain submerged for months. Behind them is a windowless steel sphere in which sits the nuclear reactor that furnishes the power for the submarine and for whatever tasks it must carry out on the bottom. Four massive articulated manipulator arms lie folded against the submarine's hull, each near a rack of tools.

Running between submarine and trawl is an umbilical cord, a thick cable of electric wires held above the trawl on a tall, retractable mast and running into the conning tower of the submarine. On the same mast that carries the umbilical cord into the trawl is a battery of floodlights, their blaze dimmed and diffused to the men sitting in the submarine forty feet away. But the water is clear, and the sand and debris stirred up by the trawl is quickly pushed out of the line of vision by the swift current. The forward end of the tank-like trawl looks like a bulldozer, extending a sharp horizontal blade that bites under the pavement, which breaks up into irregular slabs. The slabs slide up a ramp, under a series of hammers that break them into small chunks, and then into a hammermill that pulverizes them into fine particles. Mixed with the sea water, the crushed ore forms a slurry that enters a complex Christmas tree of valves

and hydraulic lines. These feed into the last large structure
that lies between the crawler treads of the tank, a scrolled
case that clearly contains a centrifugal pump.

Through the earphones on their heads the men can hear
the high-speed whine of the pump picking up the slurry of
ore and water and forcing it up the pipe that disappears
upward into the gloom.

The bottom is hard and slippery, and occasionally the
treads fail to grip. As the tank swerves slightly from its forward path, the man in the left-hand seat touches his joy
stick. The tank resumes its job of eating a straight ten-foot-
wide furrow of manganese into the infinite gloom.

It's all very dull and prosaic, as a proper industrial process
should be.

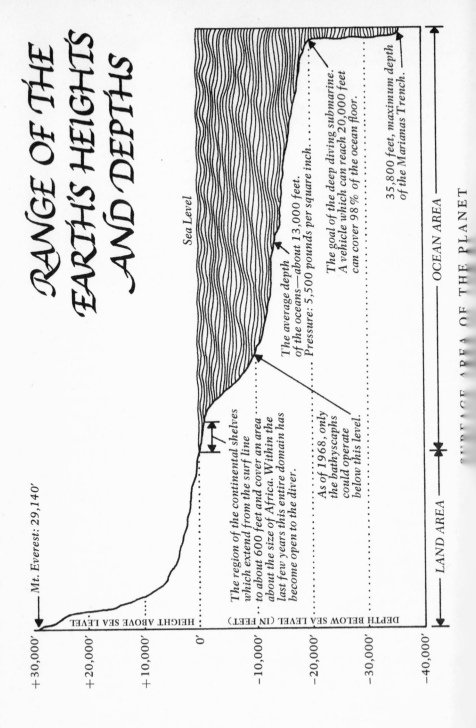

RANGE OF THE EARTH'S HEIGHTS AND DEPTHS

Mt. Everest: 29,140'

Sea Level

The region of the continental shelves which extend from the surf line to about 600 feet and cover an area about the size of Africa. Within the last few years this entire domain has become open to the diver.

As of 1968, only the bathyscaphs could operate below this level.

The average depth of the oceans—about 13,000 feet. Pressure: 5,500 pounds per square inch.

The goal of the deep diving submarine. A vehicle which can reach 20,000 feet can cover 98% of the ocean floor.

35,800 feet, maximum depth of the Marianas Trench.

HEIGHT ABOVE SEA LEVEL

(IN FEET) DEPTH BELOW SEA LEVEL

+30,000'
+20,000'
+10,000'
0'
−10,000'
−20,000'
−30,000'
−40,000'

LAND AREA — OCEAN AREA

SURFACE AREA OF THE PLANET

Submarines for Science and Industry

It is a lot cheaper to explore the sea than it is space. For $5,000 you can now buy your own submarine which will let you explore down to 200 feet—and we had better be ready for international implications. Sooner or later, someone in his own home workshop is going to build a plastic bubble and be able to descend to the floor of the ocean. It is as simple as that.
—Dr. John A. Knauss, *Dean of the School of Oceanography, University of Rhode Island*

THE AVERAGE COST of a dive to 6,000 feet in a small submarine such as the *Alvin* was, in 1966, about $4,500. The total cost of running an undersea exploration in the open sea—support ships, maintenance crew, pilots, food, and supplies—runs to $100,000 or more a month. That is indeed dirt cheap by comparison with space exploration.

Small, high-performance submarines, if driven by batteries and electric motors, are not particularly complicated in an absolute sense, although they are still fairly expensive. In part this is a result of their very limited-production, custom-built character. Intrinsically, an air-conditioned limousine with powered transmission, steering, and brakes and with a hi-fi stereo, TV, and bar in the passenger compartment is more complicated. At least it is put together from a greater number of precision parts.

Without a doubt, one of the compelling reasons that has led several large airframe manufacturers and at least one major builder of electrical equipment into the design and manufacture of prototype undersea craft and has strongly interested the established builders of military submarines is their potential for production in substantial numbers. With relatively minor exceptions, *Alvin I, Autec I* and *Autec II* are all very much alike. The U.S. Navy's first DSRV (*Deep Submergence Rescue Vehicle*) will apparently be followed by at least five others. Others examples of serial production from one basic design already exist.

It is an encouraging trend. The entry of newcomers into the field of submarine construction has sharply accelerated the rate at which new materials, new equipment, and new design concepts are being tested. The increasing availability of high-performance submarines that can take scientists and engineers deep into the ocean has not abated demand for them. On the contrary, the more small submarines that are being launched, the more the demand for their services seems to grow. It is a trend that, twenty years ago, would hardly have been anticipated.

In the history of the submarine 1948 can be regarded as the year of genesis for this new era. This was the year when Auguste Piccard launched the FNRS 2, the first bathyscaph and the first free, more or less mobile device ever built by man that would reach into the deepest ocean abyss. (The FNRS *1* was a balloon.)

The burst of submarine building that followed and is continuing at an accelerating pace is potentially the most important chapter yet to occur in the history of submarining. In order to see it in perspective, it is necessary to review its history, which until World War I was the history of the military submarine. The early submarines were aimed at a military market because that was all that existed, but in them can be seen the genealogy of the scientific and work submarine of today. A brief account of these vessels may make for dull reading, but perhaps it will temper any undue exuberance about the ingenuity of twentieth-century man.

During the American Revolution, David Bushnell, a Connecticut Yankee, and a Yale graduate whose classmates regarded him as not being sufficiently vocal in his patriotism, designed the tiny, hand-propelled *Turtle*. In this prototype submarine were embodied a whole series of major inventions, imperfectly carried out by the poor materials and the limited technology of the day. Like a modern submarine, it carried trim tanks, flooding valves and pumps. It had a depth gage, ventilating tubes equipped with crude check valves to keep water out if a wave washed over. And like the very latest research submarines, it could drop a keel weight of several hundred pounds in an emergency. Ezra Lee, a volunteer sergeant from the Revolutionary Army of almost fantastic stoicism, was taught by Bushnell to operate the hand propellors and other appurtenances of this improbable craft. Though it failed to sink any British men-of-war it did frighten them into shifting their anchorage. In one area of undersea technology, however, Bushnell was decisively successful. He was the first to demonstrate by experiment how to explode gun powder underwater, which gives him a strong claim to being the father of underwater ordnance. There is no question that he did all this for patriotism. He certainly didn't get any money from the government.

Not until 1864 when, during the Civil War, the Confederate submarine *Hunley* (still hand-propelled) sank the Union frigate *Housatonic*, did a submerged attack on a surface ship succeed, if that is the proper word. The *Hunley,* which had already drowned a couple of crews in practice, was herself destroyed in her one and only military mission. At the end of the Civil War nine similar submersibles were found in Charleston, remnants of the first submarine fleet ever built.

By 1800 Robert Fulton was trying unsuccessfully to interest the governments of the United States, Britain, and France in his *Nautilus,* a name that has become illustrious in submarine history.* Jules Verne called his fictional submarine the *Nautilus.* Sir Hubert Wilkins so renamed the old vessel with which he tried unsuccessfully, in 1931, to voyage under the ice to the North Pole. The most famous *Nautilus,* however, was the third of that name in the United States fleet and the first anywhere to be driven by nuclear power.

The first genuinely successful submarines are generally regarded as those of John P. Holland and his rival Simon Lake, which were built about the turn of the century in this country. However, American, French, Swedish, British, Russian, and Spanish designers had made numerous attempts from the 1860s on to produce a successful underwater vehicle. Steam engines for underwater propulsion had proved uniformly ineffective. In 1863 a 420-ton submarine was built in France. Driven by compressed air, it was abandoned because of its slow speed, short endurance, and general unwieldiness. By the mid-1880s, however, and with the introduction of battery-powered electric motors for underwater propulsion, the submarine began to evolve rapidly toward practical levels of performances. France alone con-

---

* Fulton's *Nautilus* was a considerably more practical craft than Bushnell's *Turtle* and actually blew up a hulk furnished by the French government. Yet the universal (and correct) military judgment of the day was that the submarine was not yet ready for action.

structed twenty-nine electrically driven submarines between 1886 and 1901. Many of these designs incorporated ideas still in use in today's small subs.

Although most of these nineteenth-century submarines were aimed at the military market, the world's navies (except for unsophisticated powers like the Turks) sensibly refused to buy these cranky and ineffective crocks. By the second decade in the twentieth century, however, submarine fleets existed, deadlier, in fact, than their owners realized. Several of the submarines' inventors envisioned peaceful uses, but the still-embryonic science of oceanography could provide few missions. Commercial applications, although by no means nonexistent, were inhibited by the limited and uncertain performance of these early craft and by the lack of all the auxiliary systems—navigation, communication, and so on—that were necessary for economic operations. The total technology to support a nonmilitary submarine industry did not exist.

Some time after Bushnell's abortive assaults on the British fleet, Washington wrote to Jefferson, "I thought and still think that it [the *Turtle*] was an effort of genius, but that too many things were necessary to be combined to expect much against an enemy who are always on guard."

If the enemy is taken as the ocean, and "things" are interpreted as all the varied devices a submarine must carry, Washington had explained why the submarine had to wait until the twentieth century for its success. It is such things as the diesel engine, the gyro compass (which with some justification has been said to have made the submarine a practical device—at least the skipper now knew where he was going), two world wars in which the submarine was a major component, and the accelerating march of twentieth-century technology, that has brought the submarine to its period of supremacy. The watershed was World War II.

The bathyscaph, whose trials in 1948 ushered in the era of deep-ocean technology, was invented by Dr. Auguste Piccard of Belgium. And the *Diving Saucer—La Soucoupe Plongeante*—which in 1958 brilliantly demonstrated a whole series of design concepts for small-submarine construction and has influenced virtually every such vehicle since constructed, is the product of one of today's great innovators in undersea technology: Captain Jacques-Yves Cousteau.

As Cousteau has repeatedly stated, the oceans cannot be fully opened up until men can place themselves in their most remote recesses. In shallow areas divers and stationary platforms are useful and frequently far more efficient than a complicated undersea vehicle. At intermediate depths, for many scientific tasks and for special mining or fishing operations that consist primarily of randomly sweeping the ocean bottom, the tethered devices like trawls or suction lines will do. But for the broadest range of tasks, men must get close to the job with their eyes and their tools.

That is what is under discussion in this chapter—the manned, dry, one-atmosphere submarine; not a diving bell or a bathyscaph or a robot submarine like a torpedo or a wet submarine such as divers use, or neutrally buoyant floats that will hang indefinitely at some fixed depth at the mercy of the local currents.

Diving bells were the first undersea devices to carry men and instruments into the deep seas (and they still do). As their name implies, these are open at the bottom and expose the crew to full ocean pressure. In constrast, the hollow steel ball on a cable in which William Beebe was dropped to

3,024 feet in 1934 can keep a man at one atmosphere of pressure. Like the diving bell, however, it is tied to the surface by a cable and has no capability of independently controlled motion. The low rate of progress in manned exploration of the sea in the prewar period is indicated by the fact that Beebe's record stood until 1950. The wet submarines are not much more than underwater motorcycles for scuba divers. As submarines go, they are truly midgets, frequently weighing less than a ton in air. Because a fully equipped diver can swim at only about one mile an hour, with considerable exertion (and provided he is not bucking a current), the efficient way for him to move any considerable distance is by riding in a vehicle. The U.S. Navy calls them, accurately if ponderously, free-flooding swimmer-delivery vehicles. These wet submarines do not have a pressure hull. Some do provide a canopy. Otherwise, the diver is fully exposed to the enervating cold and pressure of the sea. As long as they must use ordinary lead-acid batteries, even the provision of enough electric power to heat the diver's suit can strain the limited payload capability of these small crafts. A few navigation instruments; a relatively small battery, motor, and propeller; and a primitive ballasting system produce a vehicle that, in its simplest versions, costs less than an automobile. They are limited to whatever depths the diver himself can withstand.

Here attention will be focused on the true, high-performance, manned submersibles intended for work in deep water. Most of these vehicles have far greater depth capability than military submarines, for the very good reason that they would have relatively little ocean bottom to explore if they did not. The current official aim of the United States man-in-the-sea program is to develop techniques for

permitting divers to operate down to about 1,000 feet. This
is deeper than most military submarines yet go. A research
or industrial vehicle that can go no deeper can provide
greater endurance and range than a diver, puts far less physical stress on the pilot, and can carry a greater payload of
equipment, but is restricted basically to the same small percentage of ocean. The amount of ocean bottom above 1,000
feet, while the size of a major continent in its entirety, is less
than 10 percent of the total ocean area.

Because small deep-diving submersibles now exist by the
score and the rate at which they are being built is increasing,
it becomes rather monotonous to attempt to describe them all.
Here attention will be focused on the bathyscaphs, Cousteau's *Diving Saucer,* the *Alvin,* and the *Aluminaut,* all to
one degree or another innovating designs. These are repre-
sentations of the vehicles in the first generation of deep-diving craft. A second generation of vehicles, more carefully
tailored to specific work assignments, more refined in their
design, is already appearing, but embodies few radical innovations except for the "small" nuclear propulsion plant in the
NR 1. And that represents freedom from economic con-
straints, rather than an excess of ingenuity. Although first-
generation vehicles have frequently been pressed into salvage
or maintenance assignments, this has been through necessity,
not because they had been specifically designed for such jobs.

What is the difference between a research submarine and
a work submarine? One generalization is that work boats
tend to sacrifice depth capability in order to carry more
manipulators, more tools, and more facilities, such as lock-
in, lock-out compartments, for handling divers.

The first bathyscaph FNRS 2, although a technical failure,
showed that the oceans were open to exploration down to

their deepest abyss. The *Diving Saucer,* though of limited depth and endurance capability, was the first agile, convenient, relatively simple—in fact, the first truly practical—platform for underwater studies. *Alvin* was of substantially higher depth performance than the *Saucer* and was the first craft to be designed for and used by an American oceanographic institution.

Whereas most of these earlier submersibles stayed within the state of the art in hull materials, *Aluminaut* represented a significant experiment toward new and indeed radical solutions of the hull problem. Since then a widening array of exotic materials, from extremely high-strength maraging steels to boro-silicate glass, have been used for pressure hulls. As for the NR *1,* its compact nuclear reactor will demonstrate to what degree unlimited endurance frees a small submersible of dependence on support ships, and in other ways makes it a more efficient oceanographic tool.

Appropriately, the submersible that ushered in the new era of scientific and industrial deep-sea vehicles, the bathyscaph, was from the beginning capable of reaching the greatest known depth in the oceans. A clumsy and limited craft, it appears to have served its purpose, and may already be on its way to oblivion.

Dr. Auguste Piccard had conceived of the bathyscaph (Greek for "deep boat") while a student, long before he started his historic balloon ascents into the stratosphere. In 1937 Piccard requested funding for the building of his first underwater vehicle from the Fonds National de la Recherche Scientifique (Belgian National Fund for Scientific Research). He got $25,000 with which to build the FNRS 2. The FNRS *1,* also funded by the Fonds National, was Piccard's stratospheric balloon. As design and testing got underway, World War II broke out, and the project stopped until 1945. In that year his $25,000 fund was reinstated, but something called inflation had occurred in the intervening years, and the FNRS 2 that emerged in 1948 had been stripped of many useful features.

The FNRS 2 was also a balloon, one capable of rising and descending in an ocean of water rather than in an atmosphere of gas. In the atmosphere, Piccard used gases lighter than air, such as hydrogen or helium, to lift his gondola and payload. In water he used gasoline by the thousands of gallons, confined in a thin-metal tank. With the buoyancy thus achieved he could lift the small but heavy steel sphere by which the two pilots were protected from the deep-ocean environment. (Hydronauts continue to complain that they have less space per man than do the astronauts.)

Because liquid hydrocarbons, like the gasoline used by most of the bathyscaphs and the hexane used by the French *Archimede,* are substantially lighter than sea water (about 30 percent), the bathyscaphs as a class have been capable of fairly large payloads, considerably larger than those of the early and research submarines. The latter, of course, must depend on the buoyancy of their pressure hulls or on syntactic foams. These rigid foams take quite a beating, are very sturdy, and are correspondingly heavy.

The early bathyscaphs used their weight-lifting capabilities to compensate for the relatively crude pressure spheres in which the crew were housed. The sphere that Piccard obtained from Krupp for his *Trieste I* weighed fourteen tons and was far too heavy to float. Today's materials and techniques could provide the same space and protection with less than half that weight.

The parallel with ballooning extends to the manner in

which a bathyscaph rises or descends. To lighten itself, the bathyscaph drops steel shot, just as a balloon drops sand. In a 20,000-foot dive, a bathyscaph must expend up to ten tons of shot. To make itself heavier, a bathyscaph releases gasoline, just as a balloon siphons off helium. Because a fully loaded bathyscaph can weigh up to 200 tons, the amount of gasoline that must be released can be impressive, particularly to its expedition's purchasing agent: 2,000 gallons for a routine dive. The amount that must be loaded initially can reach 40,000 gallons.

The FNRS 2 had only one trial at depth. Unmanned, she was dropped down to 4,500 feet and successfully returned to the surface. But Piccard, who realized that the gasoline would automatically remain at equal pressure with the outside water and therefore could be contained in a very thin and light tank, had underestimated the beating this thin shell would take from the waves. The bathyscaph had gone down under quiet surface conditions. By the time it had been brought back to the surface, however, a stiff sea had arisen. The support ship could not pump the gasoline out of the float or hoist the massive vehicle on deck in sufficient time. It was an understandable difficulty. In later dives it took up to five hours to get a line on the craft, pump it dry, and get it on board.

Badly battered by the waves, the float was damaged beyond practical repair. It is perhaps not irrelevant that many deep-sea fish, which live comfortably in water under thousands of pounds per square inch of pressure and are sometimes enveloped throughout their normal lives in thick shrouds of gelatinous material, can be torn into ragged shreds if exposed to the waves on the ocean surface. Today the bathyscaph floats are of sufficiently shiplike form to permit moderately rapid towing, are quite rigid, and are heavily compartmentalized, so that a small puncture will not necessarily mean disaster.

The point, however, had been made. In 1950 the French Navy built a sturdier bathyscaph, the FNRS 3, which in 1954 descended to 13,282 feet. Piccard, assigned to the French Navy as a consultant on the FNRS 3, but not comfortable in that role, withdrew and proceeded to build the *Trieste I*. The *Trieste* was launched in 1953, was charted by the U.S. Office of Naval Research in 1957, and was purchased by the U.S. Navy in 1958. On January 3, 1960, (then) Lieutenant Don Walsh and Dr. Jacques Piccard, son of the inventor, dropped the *Trieste* into what is believed to be the deepest trench on this planet's surface, the Challenger Deep in the Pacific, which bottoms in the vicinity of 35,800 feet, almost seven statute miles from the surface. *Trieste I* continued to dive in the Pacific until the *Thresher* went down on April 10, 1963. By August 1963 it had made 128 dives, was 10 years old, and was worn out from hard use. It was completely rebuilt by the U.S. Navy in the mid-1960s. It received a new, sturdier, and more streamlined float, new pressure spheres, and a more powerful set of batteries and propulsion motors; and was thereafter designated *Trieste II*. Its primary use in 1969 was in training new personnel and evaluating new equipment.

The next stage in the progress of the scientific submarine began in 1959 when Cousteau launched the *Diving Saucer*. Its maximum depth of 1,000 feet was insignificant compared to that of the bathyscaph and small compared to the larger and more elaborately engineered designs that came later. Its speed of about a knot was not much more than what a diver could swim unaided. Its endurance was about four hours. Its virtues, however, became evident upon use. It was small so that it could be trucked or flown quickly to any spot on earth. (Several years later *Alvin*'s width of eight feet was set not by any abstruse principles of hydrodynamics but by the desire to move it by truck.) The *Saucer* could be launched by a crane from support ships as small as eighty feet in length. And support ships are what chew up the appropriations for diving expeditions. It was highly maneuverable. (In recovering the H-bomb from a rough and heavily silted bottom, *Alvin* accepted the lion's share of the work, in part because it could turn in a shorter radius than *Aluminaut,* and on several occasions still greater maneuverability might have shortened the recovery process.)

To a work or survey submarine, the ability to hover over an object and observe it closely, the ability to turn quickly, to slide in and out of narrow canyons, or to work under an overhanging cliff, are far more important than speed. Another vital necessity is good visibility. The ultimate in this respect is the all-glass hull. But Cousteau had to work with steel. He equipped the *Saucer* with two large plexiglass ports looking forward and down and a smaller one to view directly forward. (One small submarine whose design postdated the *Diving Saucer* was significantly limited in operational use because it has only one viewing port.)

The *Diving Saucer* mounted every possible piece of equipment outside the pressure sphere. Batteries in oil-filled cases, motors, lights, and controls were exposed to full sea pressure and protected against mechanical damage by a fiberglass casing. Only the two crewmen, the life support system, and a few key instruments were inside the pressure hull. This permitted a smaller and therefore lighter sphere; moreover, accidents that befell the exterior equipment, such as short circuits in the batteries (and there were several), did not directly endanger the crew. The *Saucer* shifted mercury, the densest of fluids, to change pitch. In an emergency, the *Saucer* could jettison a 400-pound weight and the 275 pounds of mercury to help free her from some obstruction on the bottom.

Since it first went into the water, the *Diving Saucer* has made many hundreds of dives. Its trials were run in the West Indies. The areas it has explored since then include the waters above 1,000 feet in the Mediterranean, the Red Sea, and the steeply dipping shores of California.

Relative to the vastness of the ocean, its dives are mere pinpricks, but its productivity, at least as a search device, is far greater than that of a pair of free divers. At depths below 200 feet the time on station of a free diver starts to be measured in minutes unless he is working under saturated conditions and can return to a pressurized habitat. He is limited in the area he can cover by his muscular endurance unless he uses a wet submarine or a motorized tug. However, mobility provided by tugs can be more theoretical than real. As yet, the need to stay warm and to remain in voice contact with the surface tethers many commercial divers to a bottom station by hot-water pipes (to warm their suits) and telephone lines.

The observer in a submarine can stay dry and reasonably warm, breathing air at atmospheric pressure, until the batteries in the vehicle are exhausted. Furthermore, the *Saucer* demonstrated that a small submarine could carry an array of instruments quite beyond the capacity of a diver. For example, the *Saucer* routinely mounts up to seven powerful lamps, some drawing a kilowatt apiece, and two or three cameras. On the other hand, a diver can reach out with his hands to pick up a specimen or use a tool. The *Saucer* carries a mechanical arm—a manipulator—which is ingenious indeed, but not yet a match except in strength for a man's five fingers.

On land, a man is a self-contained device. Give him food and shelter and he can maintain himself. Not so in deep water, either for the diver or for the small submarine with today's power plant. Part of the *Diving Saucer's* success came as a result of Cousteau's vast experience in the organization and day-to-day operational problems of oceanography. He knew that an adequate support ship was vital, and he had one in the *Calypso*.

On the stern is the hydraulic crane for launching and retrieving the *Saucer*. This crane demonstrates reason for the vitality of the small submarine: its ability to draw on the entire technology of the twentieth century. The crane is a commercial product used ordinarily to swing a large back hoe or scoop on earth movers. Its rigid arms help prevent the submarine from banging into the hull of the support ship. At first the crane was equipped with one open hook. Later an automatic hook used routinely for helicopter pick-up and release of heavy loads was found safer and more convenient. With this apparatus, the *Saucer* has been retrieved in sea states up to four, that is, in waves up to eight-feet high. The powerful flash lamps on the *Saucer,* invented by Dr. Harold E. Edgerton in the 1930s for high-speed photography, have permitted its location and retrieval at night. Sonar and radio tracking have permitted dives in thick fog. (These submarines, however, can and do get lost.)

To the degree that a submarine can use proven equipment and techniques whose development costs have already been amortized, it becomes a less expensive, more reliable device. To the degree that it is usable on schedule under a wide variety of conditions and over a large part of the year, it keeps operating costs down and widens the kinds of tasks to which it can be usefully applied. Scientists, like profit-making organizations, live on budgets.

In 1962 the Woods Hole Oceanographic Institution obtained sufficient funds from the Office of Naval Research to build its first submersible. This was the *Alvin,* a two-man submarine capable of reaching 6,000 feet. It has been said of the men who have attempted long-term oceanic voyages in small boats that they could be divided into two distinct groups: those who were experienced sailors and knew the sea, who made it; and those who didn't. The staff at Woods Hole—the physicists, geologists, chemists, biologists—knew in detail the kinds of experiments they wanted to run, where and at what depths, the instruments they needed, how much space and time they required.

Size was determined by transport requirements. The submarine had to be small enough and light enough to sit on the decks of the Woods Hole oceanographic ship. That kept its length to twenty feet and its desired weight to about 11 tons. Its final weight turned out to be about 13½ tons. It had to be narrow enough to get into a truck. That kept its width to eight feet. An operating depth of 6,000 feet was chosen—a compromise between the desires of the scientists on the one hand and the engineering and financial problems raised by increased depth capability on the other. This depth capability permits the *Alvin* to explore all the continental shelves, part of the continental and island slopes, and many sea mounts—in all, about one-sixth of the ocean's area. Although not a large slice of the total ocean, it contains most of its biological life, has the strongest influence on weather and ship operations, and holds the most accessible mineral deposits.

There was no point in designing for high speed. Unless a small submarine is to be equipped with a nuclear reactor (which raises the submarine's cost from a few hundred thousand dollars to many millions of dollars) or with fuel cells (which, though a hope for the future, are still very expensive), it must use electric batteries for propulsion. A submarine on electric batteries can't really go anywhere, at least not in comparison with the dimensions of the seas. Such submersibles, in sharp contrast to military submarines, must be carried or towed to the area where they will operate. Essentially, they go up and down, not sideways. That, of course, is a mild exaggeration. *Alvin* was designed for a nominal range of about twenty-five nautical miles, less than most housewives would accept for a vehicle to go shopping in. *Aluminaut,* a substantially larger craft, can go about three times as far.

Aggravating the inability of these small submarines to carry much propulsion energy is their generally indifferent streamlining. This is no criticism. Their shapes are a compromise between innumerable design problems and limited budgets. From the point of view of streamlining and low drag, *Alvin's* shape was nothing much when it emerged from the shipyard. As additional rigid buoyancy material (syntactic foam) was added later on, it began to look, in the words of Dr. Earl Hayes, who then directed its operation, like a very lumpy blowfish. In practice its practical speed limit is about two and a half knots (it could probably beat a troop of Cub Scouts on a hike) and its endurance about eight hours. Considering the size of its pressure sphere, its pilots are undoubtedly happy that its endurance is not longer.

This key structural element, the pressure sphere, was manufactured from medium alloy steel with a yield point of

100,000 pounds per square inch, the best that could be done safely in 1962. This sphere, which is *Alvin's* personnel compartment, command post, and observation station, is just under eighty inches (six feet six inches) in diameter. Observers who occasionally must recline in order to look out of the lower portholes have been known to complain that the pilot used them for a carpet. To be specific, most of the small submarines so far constructed have provided free volumes of from thirty-five to sixty cubic feet per man. The Gemini space craft provided about fifty-three cubic feet per man. A warden who placed an obstreperous prisoner in as small a cell would be accused of inhuman conduct.

The fact that the small submarines having spherical hulls are of relatively short endurance—rarely more than eight hours—and that the submarines of longer endurance, such as the *Aluminaut,* the NR 1, and the PX 15, have cylindrical shapes is therefore not entirely a coincidence. Although many factors are involved, an advantage of the large cylindrical hull (though it is structurally less efficient) is that it offers more space for the crew and internally housed equipment.

To propel and maneuver the *Diving Saucer,* Cousteau had used hydraulic jets that could be rotated by the pilot. *Alvin* used three sets of propellers directly coupled to electric motors. The units can be swiveled to thrust in any direction. Other solutions have been resorted to, none as yet ideal. These small craft need maneuverability while at very low speeds or when standing still. The conventional method of maneuvering with rudders is not open to them; rudders, like airfoils, must be moving through the water at considerable speed in order to produce useful control forces.

As in the *Diving Saucer,* everything that does not have to

be inside the pressure hull is outside. The original batteries for *Alvin* weighed about 3,700 pounds in air. In sea water they weigh only 2,000 pounds. They can of course be jettisoned if necessary.

Deep-diving submarines face some special problems in changing their buoyancy at depth. The *Diving Saucer* was sufficiently small to resort to a very simple procedure. Normally it drops a fifty-pound iron weight to surface. *Alvin* adds a 200-pound lead weight to descend and drops a 100-pound weight to ascend. *Alvin* also contains conventional ballast tanks, which can be blown (emptied) by compressed air. This is done routinely on nearing the surface to give added freeboard, very useful for the crew getting in and out of the submarine in choppy water. *Aluminaut* and several other deep-diving research submarines use basically similar techniques.

Although *Alvin's* air supply is at sufficient pressure so that the ballast tanks can be blown at 6,000 feet, air gets denser as it is compressed, so that to blow tanks with compressed air becomes less and less effective with increasing depth of operation. Although one of the results of the *Thresher* disaster was to increase the blow capacity at depth of some military submarines, this is not an ideal method at great depths. Nor does the dropping of weights appear to be a practical solution for a military craft. For the military, this is as yet a problem in search of a solution.

Not only can *Alvin* drop its batteries in an emergency; it can also dump the 600 pounds of mercury used normally for fore and aft trim. In a real jam, the pilot could unscrew the pressure sphere and forebody, which together are several hundred pounds of buoyancy, from the rest of the hull and bob to the surface. Self-buoyancy of the pressure vessel that contains the crew is the ultimate safety factor in small-submarine design.

One would think that were the sphere to be recovered after such an event, it would pretty much be the end of *Alvin* as a submarine. However, the design, construction, and test of a pressure sphere is such a time- and money-consuming effort that the sphere becomes, in a real sense, the core of the submersible. During the construction of *Alvin* three spheres were built. One was to be used in *Alvin,* one was a spare, and one was to be tested to destruction. Because the last sphere was still in fine shape after having reached the required overpressure, the Navy was left with two good extra spheres. In 1968 submarines were built around both these spheres, the *Autec I* and *Autec II.* One or both will be used in the Tongue of the Ocean, in the Bahamas, to maintain the deep water instrumentation on the Autec range.

The *Aluminaut,* a contemporary of *Alvin,* was an attempt to break the depth barrier imposed by the available steels of the early 1960s. *Aluminaut* is built of massive forged rings of aluminum alloy, each ring being slightly over eight feet in diameter, with walls six and a half inches thick. To weld such sections together with the degree of reliability and long-term life required was an essentially untried art. Therefore, the sections were bolted together, a procedure that left some of the more tradition-minded submarine designers quite shaken. As with glass hemispheres, which also cannot be welded, joints must be gasketed, butted together, and clamped. As the hull goes deeper, the joints get tighter. Several years of diving and its performance off Palomares has shown that this type of hull can be used with confidence.

An issue of the utmost legal and economic importance to manufacturers and users of submarines is that the U.S. Navy requires any vehicle carrying naval or government personnel to be "certified." Without this certification insurance companies are reluctant to cover the risk and, when they do, impose higher premiums. And if anyone fusses about the premiums on automobile insurance, he should buy himself a submarine. Certification consists, first, of careful analysis of the drawings to see if the design is safe. This is the "design audit." Then follows a "material audit" to see if the submarine was, in fact, built to the drawings. Next the method of operation, the maintenance procedures, and the training of the pilots are reviewed. It is an expensive and time-consuming operation and one that very few "back-yard" builders can comply with. Some professional societies, such as the Marine Technology Society and the American Bureau of Shipping, are investigating simpler procedures that would indicate when underwater craft meet at least minimum recognized standards of safety.

A cylindrical hull can increase crew comfort, and is helpful for streamlining and for convenient placement of internal equipment. But it imposes a weight penalty, for a sphere needs about one-half the material of a cylinder to protect the same hull volume against the same pressure. Nevertheless, the *Aluminaut* hull has a substantial "excess buoyancy," the amount of lift over and above its own weight.

Excess buoyancy at great depth is a goal that involves more than safety. Because, for a given size of submarine, the weight of the propulsion system, life support equipment, and instrumentation is roughly a constant regardless of depth, the heavier the hull, the less the payload. The real trick is not just to reach a given depth, but to do so with enough reserve of buoyancy so that an adequate number of crew, instruments, and tools can be carried.

Because these research submarines are both small and relatively inexpensive, there is much less reluctance and far more incentive to try newer materials than with large military submarines. However, the variety and unexpectedness of the problems that can arise when a new material is put into use may help explain the conservatism that characterizes naval architecture. Stronger materials are not necessarily better. They may be difficult to weld, or have a tendency to distort. In a sphere six to seven feet in diameter (the usual size of hull for these small submarines) a departure from a true spherical shape of 1/16 to 1/8 of an inch in an arc length of eighteen inches can create a loss in depth capability of many hundreds of feet. Some very high strength alloys can be highly resistant to corrosion when exposed to salt water for years in laboratory experiments. But when they are also heavily loaded, they can corrode rapidly and deeply along grain boundaries, a process that has led on occasion to catastrophic failures. In one case, a very small change in alloy content removed the problem for a titanium alloy, but first this difficulty had to become known. Because of the very low frequency, high-stress cycles that characterize diving operations, it is not easy to determine the fatigue life of an alloy, another reason why naval architects prefer to have someone else do the pioneering.

But the mood is caution rather than outright rejection. Small glass spheres carrying oceanographic instrumentation have demonstrated that they can be buoyant down to 35,000 feet, very good competition indeed to the most exotic metals available in the mid-sixties. When design started on glass hulls big enough to take a crew of two, a very routine type of snag was promptly encountered. It proved difficult, until some experience was gained, to provide flawless hemispheres of the required size. Although it is not the only way to use glass, the initial and most straightforward approach is to fabricate two hemispheres that hinge together like a giant clam. The joint between them must be made pressure tight for every dive, which calls for good housekeeping, for even a grain of sand trapped as the two halves butt together can cause a leak. Fortunately if a seal is tight after the submarine has dived to ten feet or so, it tends to improve as the depth increases.

Although there is little overtly dramatic about hull materials and seals, hardly any other aspect of a submarine's design is more important to its performance. The reader's patience will therefore be stretched to cover a short description of syntactic foams, which, aside from the hollow sphere and cylinder, is the designer's chief method for providing buoyancy.

Glass has long been the principal ingredient in syntactic foams. An ordinary plastic foam, in which the voids are formed by air or gas pressure, collapses into a dense mass without buoyancy at deep-sea pressures. To make a syntactic foam, tiny hollow glass spheres, each one with a wall thick enough to withstand pressure but light enough to float, are imbedded in a plastic matrix. This gives a stiff, light material that can be machined and shaped to fit into the irregular contours of a hull, a great virtue to a hard-pressed designer. But the plastic, heavier than water, is there only to hold the buoyant glass bubbles together, and syntactic foams for use in deep water cannot lift as much as an equal weight of properly designed sphere.

The new generation of small submarines is improving performance in depth capability, visibility, and the ability to do work underwater. In propulsion, however, progress is slow, with one exception. The NR *1* will be this country's first small nuclear-powered submarine and, as such, goes in one step from an endurance measured in hours, which is typical of the present battery-powered submarines, to a capability limited only by the endurance of the crew. A power plant to give intermediate capabilities at intermediate costs would be a great advantage to the designer. Undoubtedly, the practicality of a design, like its beauty, lies in the eye of the beholder. But the final arbiter of that quality is generally some dour accountant who cannot tell a British thermal unit from a platinum electrode. As of the mid-sixties, fuel cells, radioisotope generators and primary batteries, let alone nuclear reactors, could not yet meet the automatic and drastic criteria of the open market place.

Inherently, the work submarines of the future will operate in a world market, where the prizes for success will be huge and the competition bitter. An index of countries deeply involved with the design and building of new research or work submarines is almost a parallel of the world's major maritime powers. Although the United States exhibits, probably, the most activity as of 1969, France, Japan, Canada, Great Britain, and the Soviet Union have also demonstrated that they can design and operate small submarines.

This activity is sparked by a variety of motives. An immense amount of exploration, observation, prospecting, photographing, and testing is needed before we know what is in the oceans and what problems the scientific and industrial communities face there. An experience of the Applied Physics Laboratory after they had constructed an instrumented range for the U.S. Navy off St. Croix, U.S. Virgin Islands, is typical. Although they thought they knew the nature of the bottom topography from surveys with a precision depth recorder, they later had an opportunity to go over the bottom (at 3,500 feet) in the *Aluminaut*. One area that was supposed to be a soft bottom was in reality quite hard. In another, what was supposed to be a thirty-degree slope was actually a 500-foot vertical cliff. Having seen the situation, they knew, after the fact, why one of their arrays had slipped 1,800 feet overnight. And they also learned that the bottom, in this lightly traveled area of the Caribbean, was, like many another remote and lonely abyss, sprinkled with beer cans and cigarette wrappers. This kind of experience has become commonplace because the sonar beam of a depth sounder mounted in a ship miles above the bottom cannot be made sufficiently narrow. It fans out so that it may be hundreds of feet wide where it hits the bottom. It tends to give an average depth, smearing out the contours of all but the more massive geological structures.

Another representative example occurred when a small submarine, sitting on the bottom of the Straits of Florida (where, allegedly, the Gulf Stream runs north with overpowering intensity) proved the presence of a southward flowing counter-current. The possibility of such an effect had been indicated by instruments dropped on lines from surface ships, but the observations had been dismissed as either erroneous or transient.

An index of the need for underwater work boats is the frequency with which submarines have been pulled away from their scientific assignments. Hardly had the *Alvin* been thoroughly checked out when it was shipped east to hunt for the H-bomb. Later missions were also interrupted by requests to inspect cables and other bottom-mounted equipment.

The overall demand by industry and governments for the services of small submarines has exceeded their availability. As could be expected under such conditions, new submarines are appearing rapidly. Some are larger and more expensive than the submarines that opened up this new era. Others are aimed squarely at the professional divers, or at the underwater contractor or oil-well platform operator with a tight budget. Still others are expanding the tradition of the small sports craft and may eventually be purchased for the price of a medium-size automobile.

Although amateurs are building submarines, at times of the most improbable materials, they are as unlikely to produce high-performance craft as they are to acquire a good grasp of brain surgery, self-taught. The needs of the high-performance submarine span an extraordinary gamut of technical and scientific skills. "A submarine," say its builders, "is the world's largest machined part."

At the moment the United States owns or is building more than half the manned submarines in existence, on the way, or in development. When compared to Japan's output of fast cargo vessels and mammoth tankers, this is a rather forlorn statistic. Most of these submarines are small enough to be assembled in a garage. Yet they present the kind of technological challenge that American industry has met with great skill.

The future of the research and work submarine, like the future of undersea technology, has as yet no visible end. The value of such submarines can perhaps be indicated best by an incident from the nineteenth century. In the 1880s a British naval commander sent some rock samples from Christmas Island (the one south of Java) to Sir John Murray, who had become a great marine geologist through his experiences as a member of the *Challenger* expedition (1872-1876). Realizing, from that knowledge, that these samples were rich in phosphate, he recommended that Great Britain annex the island and mine the deposit. These sixty square miles, the flat summit of a submarine mountain that had spent a good deal of its life underwater, have produced millions of tons of phosphate, and profits that could have paid many times over the cost of the *Challenger* voyage.

Cargo Submarines

Here on the coast stands a city called Hormue, which has an excellent harbour. Merchants come here by ship from India, bringing all sorts of spices and precious stones and pearls and cloths of silk and of gold and elephants' tusks and many other wares. In this city they sell them to others, who distribute them to various customers through the length and breadth of the world.

—From The Travels of Marco Polo

THE REASON that the freight ship still reigns supreme as the carrier of bulk, nonperishable cargoes is due primarily to the high density and low coefficient of friction of water. A not inconsiderable accolade is also due the shipbuilders and naval architects who have continued to increase the size, speed, and efficiency of ships. As designers approach the speed limits imposed by nature on a vessel that must move on the surface of the ocean amid all sorts of weather, they are looking hard at alternatives. The airplane is an obvious one, very successful for special cargoes and conditions. As the carrier of half of one percent of all transoceanic cargoes, it takes a rather distant second place to the ship. There is currently no third place.

To dismiss the cargo plane so disdainfully is to ignore the most potent form of overseas transport for passengers and for very valuable cargo. The plane has already become the dominant carrier of transoceanic passengers. So desperate has become the economic plight of the passenger ship, particularly if it is manned by nationals from countries with high living standards, that it is questionable how long it will survive as a primary long-haul form of transport. As a cruise ship, that is, as a moving, ocean-going hotel, it offers a unique aura that for many is irresistible. But the ship lines are now selling aura, not transportation.

That passenger fleets are being reduced in number no longer bothers the military. So far as the soldiers themselves are concerned, the emergence of airplanes with 400- or even 700-seat capacities will take care of them—provided some protected airfields are available for the planes to land on. As for the scores of thousands of tons of munitions and supplies that must accompany every division, that is another matter.

In the area of premium freight categories (cargo worth more than say, $1,500 per ton) the plane is already an important carrier, and its role is growing. In part, the plane is succeeding because it is generating cargo that, for practical purposes, can move no other way. It is pointless to discuss the plane as an economic long-haul carrier of bulk cargo. As long as airplanes run on fossil fuels such a role would defy physical law. It is impossible to run a fleet of cargo planes over an ocean route, regardless of economics, unless ships are available to bring fuel to the landing fields or unless these are lucky enough to be close to oil fields and refineries.

Similarly, it is not realistic to discuss the submarine (or the hydrofoil or the various air-cushion machines now being developed) in terms of direct competition with bulk carriers. It would be of sufficient economic significance if any of these special vehicles found a subsidiary role or a route not feasible to the standard displacement hull. The hydrofoil is al-

ready operating successfully as a fast, short-haul ferry. Engineering evidence points to perhaps a broader role in the
future for the ground effect machine (GEM) or, as it is
called in some versions, the air-cushion vehicle.

Neither the GEM nor the hydrofoil, however, has the
overall potential of the submarine as a long-haul cargo carrier on special routes that only it can deal with.

When running deep and very fast, a submarine requires
less horsepower per pound of *total displacement* than even
the most efficient of surface ships. But that is not quite the
whole story to a freight shipper or to a merchant-fleet owner.
Before we discuss the prospects of a submerged cargo carrier
in detail, let us look at some of the economic factors that any
ocean freight carrier must live with.

During the early 1800s, the small merchant ships of the
day, which rarely exceeded 300 or 400 tons' burden (and
were therefore not much bigger than the largest ships of the
Roman era nearly two millennia earlier*) required about
one man in crew for every fifteen tons of capacity. In 1965
an American automated oil tanker of modest size—say
25,000 tons deadweight (that is, cargo capacity)—required
a crew of about 33—one man for about every 750 tons of
cargo. The ratios of men to tonnage for the really large oil
tankers, some of which exceed 300,000 tons deadweight, are
astonishing. The *Tokyo Maru*, launched in 1965, has a total
displacement of 182,500 tons and can carry 150,000 tons
of oil (equivalent to the weight of two *Queen Marys*). It
carries a total of twenty-nine officers and crewmen, including three radio operators on board because of a labor-union
contract. This ship therefore requires only one man for more

---

* About A.D. 357 Constantius brought a finished Egyptian obelisk
weighing 510 tons from Alexandria to Rome.

than 5,000 tons of cargo. Tankers of 300,000 deadweight tons, with each of their fifteen holds capable of handling the equivalent of a standard T-2 tanker of World War II, have a crew of forty, fewer than the T-2 tanker.

Of course a fluid like oil is the easiest kind of cargo to handle. Dry-cargo ships, which must onload and offload freight in all sorts of odd sizes, shapes, and weights, cannot show such startling statistics. Nevertheless, dry-cargo ships also show a strong trend toward becoming bigger, faster, and more automated. A relatively recent loading procedure is to receive a truck-trailer full of freight on the wharf, lift the entire trailer on board, then offload it on the other side of the ocean. There, the trailer is hooked to another truck tractor and continues its journey to its final destination. Cargo ships are also being built to carry loaded barges, which can be dropped off near harbors with even primitive facilities for leisurely unloading while the expensive ship goes on to the next port.

When the cargo is nonperishable and part of a steady movement—which covers most of the oil, coal, ores and many foodstuffs and dry cargoes that move in international trade—and if there is only open ocean to cross, it will take a very efficient vehicle indeed to give a surface ship any real competition.

Nevertheless, for many types of cargoes, the faster the ship, the better freight rates it commands. The introduction of faster ships—and this was as true in the day of the clippers as now—has led to the generation of cargo volume that did not exist before. In other words, increased speed of transport opens new markets. The clippers rarely brought home bananas. The steamships did not bring in orchids. Furthermore, trade routes and cargoes are continually changing, and for maximum efficiency, subtle but important changes must follow in the design of the carriers. The rewards for even minor reductions in freight costs remain sufficiently sharp that great fortunes continue to be made in ocean transport. With the population of the world still rising, with the industrial nations in need of growing imports of raw materials, with old sources of supply being depleted and new ones being opened in hitherto inaccessible and untraveled regions, merchant shipping remains a dynamic and changing industry.

Shipping is therefore saturated with political and military import. Only a nation that can fight and trade simultaneously can win a major war, said Admiral A. T. Mahan. Or, in the more pedestrian phrases of a recent report to the Maritime Commission on the role of nuclear-powered shipping, "Control of bottoms through U.S. flag operation to all parts of the world and U.S. ownership of foreign flag vessels can, when coupled with other purely economic weapons such as control of certain cargoes, confer upon the United States a broad arsenal of weapons in the economic phases of the cold war."

Today, American-flag vessels must be subsidized. The costs of construction in American shipyards and the wages of American crews are so high that such ships could not otherwise survive economically. Yet high wages for American shipwrights and American sailors have been a fact since revolutionary times. In the period preceding the War of 1812, Europeans were astonished and sometimes scandalized by the high wages paid American seamen. And the Congress was insisting on American crews in American ships not long thereafter.

If the percentage of the world's ocean commerce carried in its own bottoms is the criterion, the United States reached its zenith as a maritime power in the decade preceding the Civil War. Throughout the period that culminated with the clippers of Donald McKay and William H. Webb, Yankee shipbuilders were alert to every technical improvement that could be made in hulls, rigging, or navigation. What made American bottoms attractive were fast passages and smart seamanship.

Short of growing subsidies, the only weapon with which the United States can offset its inherently high costs is technical supremacy. We do indeed have an unchallenged lead in the building of ship-borne nuclear power plants, in digital technology, in automated control. Yet at the time of this writing, American claims to technical supremacy in ship design and construction could easily be challenged. Russian and Japanese freighters had automated engine-room operations and cargo handling on at least as broad a scale as the United States. Japanese and European shipyards are, over-all, more automated than American yards and, by programing their operations intensively, continued to increase their efficiency. In 1965 Japan built 44 percent of the world's merchant ship tonnage. It is no coincidence that Japan also turned out more ship tonnage per man-hour than any other nation. Sweden, Great Britain, West Germany, and France were second, third, fourth, and fifth, in that order.

If technical supremacy in ocean transport is to be achieved along basically conventional lines, that is, by building merchant ships, the United States is likely to find the race to catch up long if not eternal. If nuclear propulsion becomes standard, or if radically new forms of ships like submarines are also profitable avenues of advance, it may be a new ball game.

Superficially, the difficulties facing an economically successful submarine are numerous, even with cargoes for which they are adapted. Liquid cargoes are the most suitable for submarines because they can be exposed to full sea pressure and thus carried outside the heavy and expensive pressure hull. Next in line are cargoes sufficiently granulated, like wheat or some ores, that they can at least be onloaded and offloaded through the small and infrequent hatches that designers prefer to put into submarines. It is not very practical to build a cargo submarine like an ore ship. The latter, by removing its huge hatches, can be opened like a sardine tin and unloaded simultaneously by a dozen power shovels.

Submarine designers get rather edgy on the subject of "penetrations," as they call the increasingly numerous holes that are required in submarine pressure hulls. Each such hole represents a point of weakness in the structure. Each is a potential source of leakage or, if big enough, of disaster.

Because in addition to all the normal equipment of a ship it must also have the tanks, valves, diving controls, and navigation equipment that permit it to operate submerged, a submarine will always be more expensive to build and probably to run per ton of capacity than a ship.

Compounding this problem is the fact that large ships tend to be more efficient than small ships. Large ships require fewer crewmen per ton of capacity and less fuel per ton-mile. It is for the very cargoes that the submarine can handle that the largest, lowest-cost ships have appeared—the enormous oil tankers, ore carriers, and grain ships that are the most extraordinary features of the world's postwar merchant marine. Size brings its own problems. Fully loaded, some of these ships have drafts exceeding seventy feet. Ships loaded to such drafts cannot pass the Suez Canal unless it is made much deeper than it now is; nor can they yet enter most of the great harbors of the world. Their beams frequently exceed one-hundred feet, thus barring them from the Panama Canal as it is currently constructed. But the other consequences of their great size are so attractive that they continue to be built.

The most efficient hull form for a submarine calls for a circular cross section. The diameter of a submarine capable of carrying a 40,000-ton cargo and of the best hydrodynamic shape (lowest drag) is about 105 feet. A few years ago there was probably not a dock on this earth that such a submarine could approach. At the cost of some increase in drag, a tanker can be built with a rectangular cross section. Between that expedient and the fact that the big surface tankers are forcing the construction of deep-water terminals, the submarine's draft problem is no longer as major an obstacle as it once seemed. In 1967 about twenty crude-oil tanker terminals already existed that could receive ships up to 130,000 tons deadweight. By the mid-1970s superports capable of handling deep-draft ships of over 300,000 tons (or submarines of somewhat smaller tonnage) will be operating in Ireland, France, Japan, Italy, Belgium, Holland, and probably the United States. In a few of these ports, tankers will be able to tie up to buoys in deep but sheltered waters and a pipeline will bring the oil ashore to a tank farm. The point that most vividly illustrates the vastness of these projects (and the size of the world's industrial technology as it begins to face the twenty-first century) is that the shuttles between the superports and the lesser ports will be tankers of up to 80,000 tons.

The problem of draft does not end for a submarine when a port capable of receiving it is opened. The very real saving in power that a submarine shows at high speed is obtained only when the submarine is free of surface effects—that is, it is down four or five diameters, to several hundred feet. To a surface ship 400–500 feet is deep water. To such a submarine as this, it is perilously shallow. A very large submarine would be forced to the surface when journeying over the continental shelves or over shallow ocean areas and would be constantly concerned about sea mounts that surface navigators need not even be aware of. A properly streamlined submarine is also a bad sea boat on the surface and almost impossible to drive at its maximum speed. It would appear that a successful cargo submarine must be a specialized ship on a specialized route.

Such, really, was the German submarine *Deutschland* in 1916. The German government was then faced with an iron blockade and saw relief only in a fleet of submarine freighters. Paul König, captain of the *Deutschland,* arrived in Baltimore from Bremen with a cargo of dyestuffs reputed to have brought more than twice the cost of building his stripped-down submarine (a profit ratio that would have occasioned little surprise in a Confederate blockade runner). He got back with an invaluable cargo of nickel and rubber. Although plans were afoot to build more submarine freighters, the entrance of the United States into the conflict cut off Germany's most important market and source of supplies. At the same time, American destroyers and the enormous minefields that American productive capacity enabled the Allies to lay down in the North Sea further restricted Germany's access to the open ocean. Faced with a basically unfavorable geography, a tightening noose of ships and mines, and a hopeless future, Germany ceased serious efforts to continue such voyages.

Military submarines have often been used, inefficient as they are, to carry supplies into beleaguered islands. The British supported Malta in this fashion. During the later stages of the Guadalcanal campaign the Japanese stripped some of their submarines of all but one gun and two torpedoes and carried up to ten tons of cargo. This was just enough to keep a division going for about two days. Up to twenty submarines were eventually used on this run. In the later stages of the Pacific war, after Japan had persuaded Germany to send some of its submarines into the Indian Ocean, a few of them made the return trip from Malaysia loaded with tin and rubber. Similarly, United States submarines ran supplies into and evacuees out of Corregidor, and aviation gas and bombs to Army fliers on Tulagi. Every war has brought the need for blockade running to whatever side did not control the local sea and air.

A permanent and economically sound route may be created for commercial cargo submarines if a year-around transportation system becomes desirable in the Arctic. Because the concept has appeared so utterly impractical in the recent past (although not to the geographers and shippers who sought so long and persistently for a northwest passage), few are consciously aware that the shortest route between the heavily populated subcontinent of Europe and the human masses of China and Japan is under the Arctic ice. The distance from London to Tokyo via the Arctic Ocean and the Bering Strait is little more than 6,000 nautical miles. By the Panama or Suez Canal it is about twice as far.

For decades, the oil geologists have been hinting that the polar areas of North America may contain some of the greatest oil fields on this earth. In 1968 a strike at Prudhoe Bay (east of Point Barrow on the Arctic coast of Alaska) appears to have uncovered what may be the single largest oil field yet found on this continent. If these Arctic regions in

North America do indeed contain some of the greatest oil fields on earth, their output is more than 1,000 miles closer to Japan and China—and several thousand miles closer to northern Europe—than the oil fields of the Middle East.

An oil company faced with the prospect of constructing such a novelty as a submarine tanker fleet will promptly think of pipelines. But from many of the Arctic islands, the route to open water is so long and the ocean so deep that pipelines (whether or not they require heating throughout the year) are a dismal alternative. A small omen is offered by the relatively salubrious conditions of Cook Inlet, in the "southern" part of Alaska. There installations for underwater pipelines have reached $300,000 per mile for relatively small diameter pipe. In warmer waters, large diameter lines run about a quarter of a million dollars a mile. The problem is rarely money. It's the need for enormous proven reserves, measured at least by the billions of barrels, and the possibility that the engineering problems to be solved in laying the pipeline may be even more radical than those of a submarine tanker.

Aided by icebreakers, which are getting bigger and more efficient, surface ships can get into many of these Arctic areas for a short and uncertain period, perhaps three months out of the year, although the continental shelf is generally so flat and wide here that they cannot often get close to a pier. Moreover, the winter ice has a monotonous habit of clearing out every structure near the shore every year. It will likewise clear out all aids to navigation.* Such conditions do not necessarily give the cargo submarine a clear field. When

---

* An acoustic transponder, ready on demand to furnish a precise position reference, has been placed on the ocean bottom, 4,000 feet below the ice at the North Pole.

tankers are plentiful and must compete hard for cargo, the bigger ones can deliver (in 1967) Kuwait crude to the United States for about 35 cents a barrel (of about 250 pounds). That is tough competition even when the tankers are limited to three months of the year.

The Soviet Union, for the most urgent national reasons, has kept the world's largest fleet of icebreakers (in numbers and size) on her northern sea route that connects Europe with Asia along the north coast of Siberia. In 1967 Russia offered the use of this route to the world's shipping, for a fee of course. To a Japanese ship, it could cut the length of a trip to London from thirty-five to twenty-two days—that is, in July, August, and September.

It may well be that the cheapest way of transporting certain bulk cargoes from the western reaches of Russia to her Far East ports is under the ice rather than through it, even if nuclear icebreakers are doing the icebreaking.

Nor is the Arctic yet a safe and easy run for nuclear submarines, although it could improve considerably in that respect if the various underwater navigation systems that have been developed were implemented in these waters. The eastern exit of the Arctic, around the northern end of Greenland, is deep and safe. In periods of heavy ice a particular hazard to large submarines is offered by the extensive shallow areas that lie on either side of the Bering Strait, which was, not so long ago, a land bridge between Asia and North America. But a trip around the Horn in a sailing vessel also had its dangers, and hundreds of ships made that passage every year for centuries until the Panama Canal was opened.

It could have been expected that Russia would put her first nonmilitary nuclear propulsion plant on an icebreaker and the United States on a merchant ship. More than tradition is involved. With her thousands of miles of Arctic coast-line and her compelling need to populate and industrialize Siberia, keeping an Arctic sea lane open even a few weeks more per year is of national importance to Russia. It may be worth repeating, however, that no icebreakers yet visualized are likely to support a year-around surface-ship route across the Arctic. American and Russian submarines, however, have demonstrated that they can operate under the ice even during the winter.

Today the Arctic sees annual pilgrimages by Canadian, Russian, and American fleets to supply their scattered stations and villages before the nine-month freeze sets in. The 1966 Canadian expeditions, for example, started in early August from both Atlantic and Pacific ports and had to be back by October. Some twenty-three ships, two of them ice-breakers, were necessary. Aboard was over 100,000 tons of cargo destined for weather stations, military surveillance posts, and many native villages where the population had grown to the point, or had aspired to a level of comfort, that they would no longer live entirely off the land. The biggest of these ports was Frobisher, near the southern tip of Baffin Island, population 1,600.

If the population around the rim of the Arctic Ocean continues to increase and if the mineral wealth of the Arctic land masses becomes sufficiently interesting to Europe and North America, submarine cargo fleets may emerge. The individual vessels may be too small and expensive to compete on the traditional ship routes but may still be capable of bringing unprecedentedly low freight rates to the Arctic.

Freight situations attractive to a submarine may occasionally originate on open water routes. These could arise from the economic incentives offered by a blockade or from some special legal quirk that restricts surface ships. To put it plainly, smuggling is a time-honored and sometimes very profitable activity. The author, who grew up in New Bedford, Massachusetts, during the prohibition era, remembers very well the low, gray silhouettes of the rumrunners nestled in long rows against the decaying piers that jutted into the Acushnet River and the aura of success that clung to their owners.

Some of the very best families on the eastern seaboard owe a considerable part of their affluence to some ancestor with a fast ship and a strong belief in free trade. Our Coast Guard was established in 1790 by Alexander Hamilton, then Secretary of the Treasury, to stamp out the smuggling that was reducing his customs duties. It was known, straightforwardly, as the Revenue Cutter Service.

The ethics of blockade running appear to depend very much on the angle from which it is viewed. Hamilton looked dourly on American shipowners who ran goods past his customs barrier. His successors were not particularly disturbed by American shipowners who ran goods past the British blockade into Napoleonic Europe. Blockade running has frequently served national aims; or, to put the matter more elegantly, paramilitary situations continue to arise in which it is desirable to take passengers and cargoes in and out of waters controlled by hostile interests. Anyone who thinks that blockade running is a thing of the romantic past should watch the maritime news. As of the week this page was being written, one area of blockade was the Eastern Region of Nigeria, which had just seceded from the rest of that country. The price for a twenty-four hour ride in an outboard canoe from Douala in Cameroon to the old slave port of Calabar in Eastern Nigeria was about $200. Against a tougher blockade, for higher stakes, what vehicle is better able to thwart the umbrella of surveillance devices now available than a submarine?

It doesn't take much of a crisis to raise freight rates so sharply that very inefficient ships become immensely profitable to run—not that submarines were called for during the Suez crisis that occurred during Anthony Eden's tenure as Prime Minister of England. However, the price (not the cost) of transporting oil from the Persian Gulf to London rose from the £2 per ton that prevailed when the canal was open to £19 per ton when the run had to be made around the Cape of Good Hope and tankers had suddenly become scarce.

England, no longer ruler of the ocean waves, is acutely aware that many nations could bar its access to parts of its own commonwealth or to ports with which it has traded for hundreds of years—thus the call by one British scientist for the design and construction of merchant submarines to "restore to England a supremacy and invulnerability at sea such as that we enjoyed from the day of Nelson's victory at Trafalgar until the development of the hunter-killer submarine." Given the hard facts of naval architecture, this is not the most general solution to British maritime problems. However, there can still be a bright future for the cargo submarine in special situations.

One of these is as an adjunct to a naval fleet—an underwater attack transport, so to speak. If a country like the United States, which has not been seriously challenged at sea since World War II, considers such an idea rather far-fetched, one can only repeat, with Santayana, that "Those who cannot remember the past are condemned to repeat it."

For all these reasons the United States, Great Britain, Japan, and Germany (and perhaps others) continue to make studies of cargo submarines. Construction has not yet started. That step will be hard, for such a craft must have a nuclear reactor, which, as of today, establishes the project as costly and, for some nations, as politically sensitive. Technical progress, however, is inexorable. If nuclear-propulsion technology continues its current rate of progress toward lower costs and weights, the day will suddenly appear when nuclear power will become the economically conventional way with which to drive large ships. A parallel situation has already arisen for power utilities ashore.

In this rapidly approaching era, when, in all probability, nuclear propulsion will be economical for many types of surface ships as well as for submarines, the latter will have to prove their capability not only to the engineers but also to some very unsentimental bankers. And, in all likelihood, they will have to do so on new and economically unproven routes. This is not the sort of pool one can ease into gingerly. That first step will probably be a big one. But the odds are strong that it will be taken.

The Military Submarine

*Pitt [then Prime Minister of England] would be the
greatest fool that ever existed to encourage a mode of
war which they who command the sea do not want
and which if successful, would deprive them of it.*
    —EARL ST. VINCENT, *First Lord of the Admiralty,
    on the subject of Fulton's* Nautilus

OF THE MANY NIGHTMARES that man, in his ingenuity, has
created to haunt him, one of the most terrifying is a great
steel shark that lies in the abyss, awaiting the word to go
forth and destroy. It is a truly twentieth-century demon—
cybernetic, computerized, technically superb. And it is im-
placably real.

A submarine lying off the tip of Greenland can strike any
part of the megalopolis that lies between Boston and Washington. Or if the story is told in Russian, a submarine lying
under the Arctic ice can rise into a polynya (an opening in
the ice sheet) to destroy the holy stones of Kiev. And since
the seas girdle the globe and bite deep into the continents,
the tale can be retold in many tongues and with many
geographies.

Nor is there much likelihood that the demon will soon be
put to rest. The revolution that resulted from the merging of
the submarine with nuclear power continues with accelerating fury. Nothing has solidified to create an assessable equi-

librium. On the contrary, the submarine today has open to it greater opportunity for technical innovation than it has ever faced before. That potential, as much as its current capability, keeps the military submarine in the focus of every maritime power's planning.

In spite of the vigor with which submarine technology is being applied to peaceful purposes, the world, as of this writing, has no cargo submarines, less than one hundred research and work submarines, and close to 1,000 military submarines. The realm of the submarine is primarily a military one and is likely to remain so for a long time. Past submarine building programs have been huge. Future ones may be larger. The forces that have so heavily eroded the power of surface navies remain in action, in fact have intensified.

How many military submarines have been built since they became a significant naval auxiliary prior to World War I is hard to compute accurately, but the number undoubtedly exceeds 3,000 and may be in the vicinity of 4,000. At the outbreak of World War I, sixteen of the world's navies owned 400 submarines. Many hundreds were built between 1913 and the armistice. Germany alone had built 372 U-boats by 1918. It is a fair guess that the various combatants had built more than 1,000 submarines by 1918.

At the beginning of World War II the world's submarine fleets were larger than in 1913; its surface fleets were smaller. During the war possibly 2,000 submarines were built. Germany alone built slightly over 1,100 between 1939 and 1945. Russia had about 250 submarines in commission in 1941, most of them long since gone. The postwar period has seen a complete rebuilding and enlarging of the world's submarine fleets.

Russia alone has built in the order of about 350 submarines during the post war period.* The United States has built about 100, most of them nuclear. Germany, England, France, and others have reestablished building programs. (The Germans commissioned their tenth nonnuclear postwar submarine in November 1967). All this is without counting hundreds of midget submarines built and destroyed over the generations.

In spite of these international evidences of faith in the submarine, two of the three great submarine campaigns in history have ended in disaster. The antisubmarine forces of the Allies triumphed over the German U-boats twice—once in World War I and again in World War II. Only in the smaller submarine action of the United States against a technically inferior Japanese defense did the underwater vessels triumph decisively. And what is the result?

Except for the United States and, to a lesser extent, Russia, the world's naval powers have ceased to construct large surface warships. The battleship is virtually a relic, suitable at best for a shore bombardment role against a country with no significant naval capability. Carriers continue to demonstrate their effectiveness in policing actions where they encounter no overt opposition, but as a factor in an all-out naval conflict, their role is entangled in controversy. No one is building cruisers. Only the submarine glides quietly forward, serenely taking a greater slice of the world's naval construction budget than ever before. It is the new "ultimate" weapon.

The British, with a delicate sense of the appropriate,

---

* The threat implied by large numbers of Russian naval units is diluted by her need, imposed by geography, to maintain four separate fleets: the Northern, Baltic, Black Sea, and Pacific.

named their first nuclear submarine *Dreadnought,* after the ship that in 1906 became the symbol of the invulnerable, omnipotent man-of-war. The *Dreadnought* of 1906 and its descendants dominated naval warfare for three decades. Then, in a series of debacles that rained impartially on the battleships of the United States, Great Britain, Germany, and Japan, it was demonstrated that new military techniques, in the shape of airplanes, submarines, radars, and ocean-spanning communication networks, had rendered them obsolete. Worse still, wars of attrition on ocean commerce, which once were no more than a nuisance to great naval . powers, now threaten the jugular veins of those nations like England and Japan that cannot exist without ships.

For the past decade the new queens of battle have been the ballistic-missile submarines. The universe is changing, said Marcus Aurelius. Obsolescence undoubtedly awaits these new underwater dreadnoughts, but the omens of their fate are not yet visible. This current "ultimate" weapon, the ballistic-missile submarine, has now grown, in the version developed by the United States, to a displacement of about 8,000 tons* and a cost, in American dollars, of about $100 million per ship.

In the U.S. Navy, about half the officers are or have been aviators. Many of the others are in surface ships. In time of peace (if the seventh decade of the twentieth century is indeed a time of peace) this navy deploys four gigantic surface fleets (the First, Second, Sixth, and Seventh). This has not prevented the submarine service from rising sharply in

---

* Displacement is the actual weight of the ship rather than a number that represents the volume or weight of cargo it can carry. The displacement tonnage of surface ships varies with the amount of fuel, stores, weapons, cargo, and anything else on board at a particular moment. The displacement of a submerged submarine is directly proportional to the volume of its pressure hull and ballast tanks.

power and influence. In World War II the submarine service absorbed less than 5 percent of the Navy's personnel. Today, it absorbs about 10 percent of its personnel, a number that does not tell the full story, for these volunteer crews represent a much larger fraction of the Navy's most capable officers and technicians.

St. Vincent's blunt comment has proved prophetic. England no longer rules the seas. No surface fleet can. The United States, whose world-spanning economic structure is lashed together by airline and merchant fleets, is entering the submarine era reluctantly and with foreboding. In spite of extraordinary progress in antisubmarine warfare, in spite of (in actuality, because of) the growth of worldwide surveillance and communication networks, in spite of ingenious homing weapons that (allegedly) can seek out and destroy a submarine no matter how deep or elusive, the nuclear-propelled submarine stands at the apex of naval might. In Russia, the United States, France, and very likely Red China, it is the focus of major building programs. To each of these nations, it represents a threat without an adequate counter.

The essence of this threat is that no one can yet discover, to a sufficient level of confidence, where the submarine is. Indeed, there are many reasons for doubting that improved methods for detecting submarines will lead to their downfall. Every known method for detecting a submarine can detect a surface ship as well or better. Radar can only see targets above the surface. Sonar can hear nuclear submarines at great distances when the latter are at top speed and can hear the obsolescent diesel-electric submarines when these are banging away with their engines. A submarine in a patrol-quiet condition, however, is close to inaudible and is therefore "invisible." A submarine on the surface with its diesels at full power makes as much noise as—and sometimes more than—a surface ship, but in this day and age a noisy submarine is a sheer stupidity. Of course there is active sonar, against which silence is no defense, but active sonar faces its own peculiar set of restrictions. Prior to World War II, the British were positive that in their active sonar (ASDIC) lay the absolute answer to the German U-boats. Admiral Karl Doenitz took very little time to prove them wrong. Satellites can see the surface ships or detect their radio emissions. They can do little with a submerged submarine. Magnetic detection, marginal in effectiveness as a search technique today, should be largely useless against very deep diving vehicles.

It is not that antisubmarine detection devices and antisubmarine weapons are ineffective in an absolute sense. Their capabilities are truly scores of times greater than those of the equivalent devices in World War II. Sonars carried by the more advanced torpedoes of today are more elaborate and of higher performance than the sonars mounted in the most up-to-date destroyers of a generation ago. The arguments of the antisubmarine forces—ships, aircraft, and submarine-hunting submarines—that they have greatly increased their effectiveness is unquestionably valid. Were they to be turned loose on the submarines of World War II it would undoubtedly be a debacle for the submersibles.

But, alas, they no longer face the same submarines. True, relics of that production period remain, their hulls growing weaker and their equipment more obsolete year by year. Every year the ones still afloat are counted in *Jane's Fighting Ships* and are quoted in assessing a country's submarine strength. But these are not the threat. In the classrooms

where antisubmarine warfare is taught and where perhaps
for the sake of morale much is made of the ease with which
snorkeling submarines can be detected, the submarine has
on occasion been referred to as the rabbit. Perhaps it was a
rabbit when, with weakened batteries, it had to evade a
charging destroyer. But if the nuclear-propelled submarine is
a rabbit, it has grown sharp teeth. It is now faster than most
surface ships and fast enough to confuse helicopters and
planes. Its weapons have become thousands of times more
powerful. No weight carrier, the military submarine has always been limited in the number of weapons it can carry. A
score of torpedoes is close to a full load. In the old days,
when it mounted guns on its decks, its magazines could hold
so few shells that a shore bombardment was a gesture. But
that was long ago, before fission and fusion became household words.

Blind and in an alien element when submerged, the submarine has profited relatively more than the surface ships
from the past twenty years of progress in navigation devices,
sonars, and computers. The surface ships have enjoyed reasonably good communications with each other and with
their base commanders almost since the days of Marconi.
Increasing sophistication in communication and telemetry
will undoubtedly affect submarine communications for the
better. In view of the past difficulties of submarines to communicate when submerged, any significant improvement in
this capability may be the beginning of something far more
threatening than the lone-wolf tactics and loose packs of
World War II.

The surface ship never had a serious life support problem.
The submarine did—one that could become desperate after
eighteen hours of submergence. This problem is not solved

in its entirety, but the whole sweep of space technology and strenuous efforts aimed at the underwater environment have done much to mitigate it. Submarines that can cross the Arctic Ocean in winter and can remain submerged for two-month patrols cannot be judged in terms of past antisubmarine campaigns.

It is fortunate for the fate of the world that peace depends more on the fear of overwhelming retaliation than on faith in the efficiency of antisubmarine warfare. The essence of the problem faced by the antisubmarine forces, were the issue to hinge on them, is that they now must be close to perfect or fail. In past wars, the submarines could be discouraged if one submarine was sunk to every three or four of its victims. Suppose, in an atomic era, that the antisubmarine forces face a fleet of fifty ballistic-missile submarines and sink forty of them. That is a fine record, a better one than many submariners will agree is possible. But what could ten loads of nuclear missiles do to a country? Would a nation at war refuse to accept the loss of four out of five of its vessels in order to deliver a death blow to its enemy? The lessons of the past speak again and again of desperate attempts against greater odds.

Whatever the actual equilibrium between submarine and antisubmarine forces—and it is one in which numbers, morale, geography, and human competence count as heavily as technical issues—the world's tacit judgment on this matter is plain. The only navies that are not building submarines as their primary strike force and as weapons with which to hunt down the enemy's submarine missile carriers are those that are economically or technically unable to do so. Moreover, today's are the largest, most expensive submarines in history.

The reason that the submarines of the United States, Great Britain, and France are so similar in size and armament is more than a desire to follow a well-defined technical path. These three countries believe their most likely threat to be the one great nation of this world whose population centers are far from the oceans.

For those whose aim is to threaten the Western powers, Japan, or China, the problem is simpler. To European nations and to the most populous countries of the East, a cheap, crude missile with a nuclear head that is carried within a hundred miles or so of the shore can be virtually as dangerous a threat as a large and sophisticated missile fired thousands of miles at sea or from a land site—not that any technical barrier exists to the size of a submarine missile. Submarines can be built much larger than they are now. Yet as we enter the era of antimissile missiles with nuclear heads exploding in space to destroy the enemy's incoming weapons, a crude, low-flying missile takes on an added menace. It could be the weapon that could most easily sneak past the enormous upward-pointing arrays of space-searching defenses.

Neither size nor numbers, however, are the critical issues in the concept of the nuclear-missile submarine. Russia's land mass, for example, is the largest in the world. It is almost three times larger than that of the United States. But by dispersing its missiles in the oceans, it will find 17 times more room than its own territory. For a country like France, the oceans present hundreds of times more room for dispersal than its own territory. France, and even more urgently Great Britain, must disperse its missiles in the oceans. Near misses directed by an enemy at hardened launch sites within their borders could just about destroy their countries.

Even a short-range missile, if carried by a submarine, can create a monumental search problem. Consider, for example, a 300-mile missile. This is a range the Germans were able to achieve in 1944. A submarine with such a weapon could hit United States territory while anywhere within a 3 million-square-mile area—approximately the size of the United States itself.

The threat of the nuclear submarine, and the growing inability of surface and air power to deal with it as it goes deeper and faster, has become one of the key reasons for building more attack submarines. It is a parody of the ecological maxim that the chief enemy of a species is its own kind. It is not the wolves that make life hard for the deer, but other deer who eat the same pasture.

The large submarine fleets of today are increasingly oriented toward the hunting of other submarines. Not that they have dropped their older missions of surveillance, of laying mines, and of attacking unarmed merchantmen. But these were basically secondary missions, which was why in the past most navies regarded the submarine as an auxiliary device. Merchant ships were relatively safe to sink. Effective submarine actions of the past have been marked by exchange ratios—that is, the ratio of the number of surface ships sunk to submarines sunk—of about 20 to 1, or rarely, over 100 to 1.

When subs hunt subs, no such ratios can be expected. The prey will now be military vessels, equipped with the best sonars their countries can provide, manned with trained crews, able and in fact anxious to counterattack. Submarines will break more teeth on such targets than they did on the exposed and generally unarmed surface vessels they formerly dealt with.

It is dangerous, or at least a gross simplification, to assume that an unlimited number of attack submarines will make antisubmarine warfare successful. In view of the new roles that are arising for the submarine and of the many difficulties submarines face in some of these missions, it is a fair conclusion that the United States, for one, is not likely to have enough of them to cover the great ocean areas it must protect. This geographic truth is at the bottom of a dilemma facing the United States Navy that undoubtedly has its counterpart in several other admiralties. Like most dilemmas, it has many focal points.

To obtain the number of submarines that the submariners feel is required to do an adequate job of patrolling, given all the other aids to antisubmarine warfare (ASW) that exist, leads to a far larger slice of a naval budget and a greater proportion of the best personnel in a navy's ranks than the other branches of the services are willing to accept. In the United States, the submarine service is already taking a very large fraction of the top half of the Naval Academy's graduating class. From this group come the greatest percentage of the officers who, in the years ahead, give vitality and strength to whatever branch of the service they enter.

To concede that a 5,000-ton nuclear-propelled attack submarine of today, with a crew of over one hundred, is many times, perhaps scores of times, more effective than the much smaller diesel-electric submarine of World War II does not solve the problem created by the ballistic-missile submarine on a planet whose surface is mostly water.

The problem is biting countries with a smaller gross national product much harder than it is the United States. That is said less in sympathy than in fear that necessity will force them to a solution unimpeded by the scores of requirements, many of them conflicting, that inhibit change in our own designs. To make the problem specific, consider the American submarine fleet of about 150 submarines. Some forty-one are ballistic submarines and not available for antisubmarine patrols. As long as they carry such large weapons, they will remain large ships.

Scores of our present attack submarines were built during World War II and, though modernized, are of limited utility against nuclear opponents. Whether nuclear or conventional powered, only about one-third of a submarine fleet can be on station at any given time, and keeping that ratio takes a bit of doing.

During a good part of World War I, the Germans had an average of about fifteen submarines at sea at any one time. In World War II, the Germans had an average of about thirty-six submarines in the Atlantic during most of 1941. In May 1942 an average of four U-boats off our Gulf ports sank forty-one merchant ships. That was when they were, in actuality, marine guerrillas, armed with chemical explosives. To fight them the Allies used hundreds of ships and thousands of planes.

"The people," said Mao, "are the ocean in which the guerrillas swim." For a submarine guerrilla, the metaphor vanishes in the literal truth. What it boils down to is that an aggressor can get by with relatively few submarines. If these submarines are very good—particularly if they are very quiet—the defender needs many more antisubmarine vehicles. This is increasingly likely to be true whatever other aids, surveillance systems, planes, satellites, buoys, and so on the defender may have. If the ASW problem were thrown entirely on the shoulders of the submarine, it is conceivable that thousands would be needed to guard countries like the United States or Russia—nations that can be attacked from many oceans. At least hundreds would be needed to guard a country like China with only one coastline. Such numbers are utterly at variance with current fleet strengths or building programs.

The effectiveness of the defense depends only partially on the performance of the satellites, surface ships, swarms of planes with their scores and hundreds of sonobuoys, and other elements of the ASW force. The significance of their role depends on what will happen to the missile-carrying submarines. If, in another decade, the missile-carrying submarine has become much quieter than it is now, if it can descend to greater depths, if it is present in far larger numbers than today, some of the traditional elements in ASW must inevitably become less significant. It is hard to see much promise in any ASW system that operates exclusively in the air or on the surface. The ASW forces will be forced to descend into the enemy's world. This will almost surely call for phenomenal numbers of high-performance attack submarines. By angering a good part of the rest of the Navy we in the United States can barely man the 150 or so submarines we have. Could a major power—in particular, could the United States—man, on a permanent basis, ten or one hundred times that number?

Thus the continued interest in small fighting submarines —not the one- or two-man midgets such as were built by the hundreds during World War II, but vessels capable of staying at sea for long periods under all weather conditions and equipped to carry out a variety of missions. (In the background is the threatening possibility that strategic nuclear weapons can be mounted on small submarines too.)

Submarines have generally been called "boats"*—to be more precise, they were originally called submarine torpedo boats, that is, torpedo boats that could submerge. These early undersea vehicles were so small that they carried, at most, one or two officers and a handful of crew. The USS *Holland,* first (in 1900) of the hundreds of submarines† that the U.S. Navy has since constructed, was fifty-three feet long and displaced seventy-four tons. Many a weekend sailor ventures out in a vessel of more majestic dimensions. Craft of such size, for whom a lieutenant was a senior officer, were obviously not ships.

Except for a brief period of giantism that affected the submarine design activities of several nations during the 1930s and that, in the case of Japan, continued throughout World War II, most submarines of the prenuclear era had displacements of less than 2,000 tons. The French submarine *Surcouf,* completed in 1934, displaced close to 3,000 tons on the surface and over 4,000 tons submerged. It was then the largest submarine in the world. During that same period, the United States built several submarines that displaced close to 4,000 tons submerged, the British had one class of submarines in the 3,000-ton range, and the Japanese by 1945 had built more large submarines than anyone else.

Many of these large submarines survived into World War II but did not particularly distinguish themselves. The Germans, even in their open-ocean forays, did very well with U-boats which generally displaced under 1,000 tons. Faced with the enormous reaches of the Pacific, the U.S. Navy

---

* One distinction between a ship and a boat is that the latter can be lifted out of the water. Today, in a parallel with the military submarines of sixty years ago, the new research vehicles are christened on the dock, then ceremoniously lifted by a crane and dropped into the water.

† Note how the descriptive adjective "submarine" has become a noun.

standardized on a submarine that displaced 1,800 tons on the surface.

In the postwar era many, perhaps most, capable submarine commanders have continued to believe that, overall, large size hinders rather than helps an attack submarine. A large ship can carry larger crews, heavier sonars, more equipment, more weapons, more amenities. (But only at the risk of involving Parkinson's law. It has been remarked, with sarcasm, that large submarine crews now require a doctor on board—and preferably one who can run a movie projector.)

Smaller submarines tend to be quieter and harder to find—acoustically, magnetically, or by Mark I eyeball.* A navy can have more of them. They can be in more places at once. From rescuing downed pilots to scouting enemy coasts, dozens of missions exist that are performed better by a small than by a large submarine.

At the end of World War II, Admiral C. B. Momsen argued strongly that the United States should develop a small submarine primarily for the purpose of stalking enemy submarines. This was the origin of the SSK (Submarine Killer) class. The aim was a ship of about 750 tons, but the three vessels built displaced over 1,000 tons each. Even so they suffered from a general overcrowding of equipment, were driven by light, compact, and, as it turned out in practice, somewhat erratic diesel engines and never behaved in the trouble-free manner the Navy expected.

Much of the impetus for continuing down this difficult

---

* Navy slang for the unassisted human eye. Virtually every piece of equipment on a military ship is designated by a Mark number, which indicates its class and chronological sequence in procurement. The human eye has not gone through any recent redesigns, a point reflected in this ironic appellation.

track was lost when, soon afterward, the *Nautilus* was launched. Its nuclear propulsion plant with its massive shielding and its relatively low-pressure, low-temperature steam plant needed a 3,200 ton hull to float it. Nuclear power plants immediately began their slow trend, still in progress, toward greater efficiency and lower weight per horsepower. On the other hand crews grew larger, sonars became more numerous and heavier, and many new features were added to the submarine's internal instrumentation.

Attack submarines came routinely to displace 3,000 and even 4,000 tons. Perhaps the history of the submarines that carry the name *Skipjack* epitomize the entire trend. The first submarine of that name in the U.S. Navy was launched in 1911 and displaced 287 tons. She carried an officer and nineteen enlisted men. (Her first commander, incidentally, was a young lieutenant named Chester W. Nimitz, later to become Commander in Chief, Pacific and fleet admiral and still later to sign the letter that gave a captain named Rickover the authority to drive forward his plans for a nuclear-propelled submarine.) The second *Skipjack* was one of the standard fleet boats of World War II, with a surface displacement of about 1,449 tons. The third and current *Skipjack*, nuclear propelled, displaces about 3,000 tons. For a while, the upward trend in size of the tactical submarine climaxed with the USS *Triton*, which carried two nuclear reactors and an enormous radar (for a submarine) and displaced about 5,450 tons. This figure was soon exceeded by the Polaris class of submarines, whose huge midsections must carry sixteen long-range missiles and which can exceed 7,000 tons in displacement. However, a new class of attack "ship," carrying no more than the conventional number of torpedoes, displaces about 4,600 tons.

In the late 1950s, Captain Richard Laning, first commander of the *Sea Wolf,* again raised the issue of the small attack submarine, this one to be nuclear propelled. He realized that, to give such a submarine basically the same capability as its larger cousin, a huge development program to reduce the size and weight of the submarine's many internal equipments, from gyro compasses to reactors, was necessary. The general consensus at that time, however, was that such a program was premature, that time had to be allowed for proper equipment to evolve without crash programs of uncertain outcome. In some of these areas, time has, in fact, succeeded more spectacularly than anyone might have dared hope a decade ago. The intertwined destinies of electronic microcircuitry and digital computers are one of the factors for this new feeling of optimism. Life-support equipment, in large part under the impetus of the space program, has become more compact and effective. Vital subsystems, a prime example being the inertial platforms and their associated computers now virtually mandatory for navigation, have enjoyed similar evolutions. The original submarine inertial platforms (SINS) were bulky and expensive. In the intervening decades two lines of development have occurred. The platforms for military submarines remain big but have improved phenomenally in performance. However, compromises on performance have permitted such reductions in size and cost that inertial navigation systems are now being mounted in commercial jet liners.

At the moment, the nuclear power plant continues, more than any other one factor, to control submarine size. It is a much longer-lived, quieter power plant than it was a decade ago, but it was still, in 1967, tied to a massive shield and to a comparatively low-pressure, low-temperature steam plant.

Breakthroughs, perhaps toward other types of reactor designs than are now used, toward thermoelectric conversion, or even toward fuel-cell propulsion, will probably come, but such technologies are not yet affecting design.

Ironically, at the very time when small nuclear submarines may be edging toward feasibility, destroyers are becoming larger and more expensive. There exists no more certain way to make the position of the surface ship more precarious. It has been remarked that if destroyers become as expensive as submarines, navies will build the latter because submarines are better antisubmarine vehicles. Such a view is a broad-ax simplification of the total destroyer mission. Yet what is the potential if such a trend really takes over and submarines become significantly less expensive, in terms of men as well as dollars, than surface fighting ships?

What the professional submariners desire are small submarines, under 1,000 tons preferably and perhaps as small as 200 or 300 tons hopefully. Such submarines are not midgets. Part of the problem of the truly midget military submarine is its inability to carry sufficient instrumentation, supplies, or weapon loads. The usually suggested remedy is a mother ship. However, attempts to compensate for such failings by means of mother ships have not yet succeeded militarily. The problems of communication and rendezvous and of launching and retrieval have been just too difficult to overcome under the unpredictable conditions of warfare and in the face of obstacles interposed by nature and a malevolent enemy.

Although in that period it still wasn't good enough, the Japanese chose potentially the best mother ship for a midget submarine: their big trans-Pacific subs. Today the U.S. Navy plans to carry thirty- or forty-ton DSRVs (Deep Submergence

Rescue Vehicles) to their operating areas "piggy back" on the deck of a nuclear submarine.

As underwater swimmers achieve greater capability it is becoming militarily more important that they be able to leave a submarine well out to sea. The swimmer-delivery vehicles—the "wet" submersibles that are required to conserve the diver's strength and bring him to his destination less exhausted—are becoming larger and better instrumented. Planned for them are sonars, navigation and communication equipment, a life-support system, and other equipment to make rendezvous after a mission a less hazardous and uncertain procedure. Like the DSRVs, these swimmer-delivery vehicles will ride on the mother submarine's deck. But "less" is a comparative word. The burden of proof remains on the proponents of a mother-midget combination.

Progress in nuclear power and fuel cells can remove the range restriction that has so far afflicted the small and even the midget submarine. It will not remove a far more fundamental problem inherent in one- or two-man crews. (This criticism does not apply to the diver vehicles or to the research submarines whose missions are measured in hours and whose support ships are constantly and solicitously hovering nearby.) Successful missions have been carried out by midget submarines, generally "one-shot" raids in which the crews accepted very high risk. In shallow water, in collaboration with increasingly effective divers, aided by improving communications, the opportunities for short-duration missions will grow. But the midgets will remain auxiliaries, incapable of successfully handling long deep-sea patrols.

Psychologists have amassed a vast array of historic and experimental evidence that a group of less than four persons is in a precarious position if it is isolated and under stress for long periods. The typical patrol period for a submarine, it may be remembered, has been in the order of two months, and many longer voyages are on record.

The small crews of airplanes and of spaceships are not yet in a parallel position. Plane flights are measured in hours, not in months. As yet the flights of spaceships are also not comparable in duration to submarine patrols. A still greater difference than duration is the circumstance surrounding these vastly different missions. The plane pilot and the astronaut can look out a window and see a world that, however changed, can still be equated to the environment in which they grew up. Both can be in frequent communication with fellow human beings on Mother Earth. The astronauts in particular have the full and warm support of an extensive organization below them. They are chosen and screened with extraordinary care and begin their journey in a state of peak morale and motivation. In the future, when they penetrate so deeply into space that contact with Earth is broken and they are alone for months or years at a time, their problems may eventually exceed those of submariners. For the moment, however, it is the latter who live in a more alien world. If submariners had a window to look out of, they would see only a chilling blackness. When they listen, they hear no human voices—only an assemblage of unfamiliar sounds.

True isolation, involving a reduction in normal sensory stimuli and compounded by the frequent threat or actual presence of danger, can drive the most normal of men quite far into the realms of hallucination, paranoia, and ineffectiveness. Experience in the Antarctic and elsewhere indicates that even with the abrasive and egocentric personalities screened out, the larger the group that is isolated, the better.

For many reasons it is difficult if not impractical to reduce the control functions of a military submarine to the point where a crew as small as that of a bomber can handle them. The time scale of the patrol, the nature of the environment, and the required flexibility of response to a wide variety of situations are not the same. At the least, the submarine needs enough in crew so that they can stand regular watches and get adequate rest. Thus, the concepts for the small submarine, when drawn up by the most optimistic of experienced submariners, tend to call for crews exceeding twelve, standing watches in groups of at least four. Submarine crews now exceed 100. To halve that number, let alone reduce it by 90 percent, would be an enormous achievement and would result in a substantial military gain to the country that did it first.

When West Germany resumed the building of submarines in the early 1960s, it began with a design that displaced 350 tons. (Later and slightly heavier versions have since been sold to several countries.) However, this submarine is driven by diesel engines and is of relatively limited endurance. Fuel cells could drive such a submarine, submerged, for several weeks. A nuclear reactor would drive it indefinitely.

Although the nuclear propulsion plant is slowly shrinking in specific weight (pounds per horsepower) and in size, inherent problems will tend to keep this a large and massive source of power. Estimates for the specific weight of nuclear power plants for spaceships have a more optimistic ring than those of submarines because the former can take advantage of such techniques as shadow shields and the use of hydrogen tanks as buffers.

In spite of reductions in the size of navigation, digital

computers, and life-support systems, not all submarine instrumentation problems will automatically yield to the magic of micro electronics. Large sonar transducers (large enough to dwarf the average living room) are more effective than small ones, and torpedoes have shown little tendency to get small. These two elements, at least, remain fairly intractable barriers to extreme reductions in size.

One of the very great contributions to small size would occur if the crew could be cut down by increased automation and by making the hordes of black boxes of a submarine less in need of constant tinkering and maintenance. One would think that were easy. But the incredible number of variations that occur in the tactical situations a submarine must meet defy simple solutions. Chess is simple compared to the deadly "games" that submarines must play, and it has taken an enormous effort to program a chess game on a computer.

Except for the power plant, no item is more weight- and space-consuming (or more expensive) on a submarine than a man. He needs a place to sit in front of his equipment, a shower, a toilet and washing facilities, a galley, a table at which he can eat his meals (even if it is used in shifts), room to move about. He needs his own bunk. "Hot" bunks—that is, a bunk used in shifts by more than one man—have occasionally been resorted to on overcrowded submarines, but always with a loss of morale. Crewmen like to eat three times a day—and plentifully. Submarines have gone to sea with even their shower stalls packed to the overhead with canned goods. Fresh food requires refrigerated space. The fresh water that is needed for drinking, cooking, and washing can come from the sea only through the installation of distillation equipment. Submarine crews, unlike spaceship crews, are in the habit of using water almost as freely as land dwellers—in the order of twenty gallons per day.

Even garbage disposal is a special problem on a submarine. No skipper would dare eject garbage so that it could float to the surface and betray the submarine's presence. As garbage accumulates, the cooks pack it in weighted bags and eject them through the equivalent of a torpedo tube. How else does one throw something overboard from a submerged submarine?

The fact that research submarines are already smaller than heavy planes and that small military submarines may not be much larger has not escaped the hawkeyed attention of the aircraft manufacturers. Generally, submarines have been built almost exclusively in shipyards. An exception occurred in the closing phase of World War II, when the Germans mass-produced complete sections of submarine hulls throughout the interior, bringing them together by train and canal for final assembly near tidewater.

The aircraft manufacturers are also aware that planes have always been designed with extreme rigor and attention to detail and with the narrowest of safety margins. Such small factors of safety are satisfactory only when every condition under which the plane will operate is known with great precision. This attention to detail persists not only for the airframe and engines but also for every piece of apparatus inside the plane. Submarines were not, in the past, designed with the finesse that has been lavished on planes. Not until recently, when submarines have really begun to dive deep, have they become weight limited. Earlier, most submarines carried tons of lead ballast to help them to submerge.

Planes have always been weight limited. If they are too

heavy they don't fly. Or at least they don't make a profit. Submarines and their subsystems are now beginning to face the same rigorous criteria for design success. The shipyards that have traditionally designed submarines may still have the edge in knowledge of submarine problems and of environments. They can keep that edge only by expending engineering and research effort as lavishly as do airframe manufacturers.

The technical problems of the submarine are sufficiently provocative and complex and the potential and frequently competitive solutions are sufficiently intriguing so that it is impossible to avoid the temptation to contemplate what may happen in another ten or twenty years. But before that is done, we must be able to list the factors that, if improved, will make the submarine a better weapon.

Aside from the overwhelming influence of the competence and daring of the officers and crew, submarine performance is affected by the capability of its sonars and instrumentation, its underwater speed and endurance, its depth capability, its noise output, its control characteristics, its weapons, and its size.

Hardly any other performance characteristic except the basic capability to run submerged is more important to a submarine than the noise it makes. It even divides its noises into categories: radiated noise (the noise it broadcasts into the water that can be heard by an enemy) and self-noise (the noise it generates to interfere with its own sonar). To say that its efficiency and survival depend on how quietly it operates is a simplification, but if two submarines are otherwise on a par in capability, the noisy one is facing some bad odds. "The armor of the submarine is its cloak of invisibility."

But one doesn't necessarily have to put a noisy power plant into a submarine. Research on thermoelectric and thermionic conversion, in which the heat is changed directly into electricity, continues to make progress. Although efficiencies are not yet impressive—and some of the semiconductor materials have shown an irritating tendency to degrade with time—a completely silent method of converting heat to power may one day (perhaps soon) become the rule on submarines. This statement assumes that a nuclear reactor will be the heat source, but suppose that, in the next decade, fuel cells become smaller and cheaper?

Probably, but not absolutely, an electric motor and propeller will still be necessary. Although in theory electromagnetic propulsion, with the magnetic fields reacting directly on the salt water around the submarine, is a possibility, this method is in its very early stages of development.

When a submarine has a quiet propulsion system and propeller, it can be quiet when it is going slowly. Magellan's ships managed to get around the world at less than four knots; Nelson chased the French fleet all over the Atlantic at probably less than eight knots. Because submarines can remain at sea for months, they can cover vast distances at low speeds and still be left with enough time to accomplish their missions. All submarines today are noisy when they run at high speed, sufficiently so that they can be heard by today's sophisticated sonars scores of miles away. One reason is that they must expend eight times as much energy at twenty knots as at ten knots; over sixty times as much energy at twenty knots as at five knots. The faster any vehicle goes through the water, the more turbulence it makes, and the more noise. As the submarine goes deeper it can reduce but not eliminate these problems.

Here is where meticulous streamlining of every little hole and protuberance—the sort that goes into a jet plane—is of the essence. A near-perfect form cuts down on drag so that less horsepower is required to drive it. Perhaps that doesn't matter as long as power is cheap. But more than the availability of construction money is involved. Bigger propulsion systems, no matter how carefully made, require bigger auxiliaries, which make more noise. They also require bigger hulls. Bigger hulls draw more water. It is hard enough to get submarines in and out of harbors now, but that difficulty is trivial compared to the problems that much smaller submarines have encountered in fighting in shallow water. The big submarines of today are deep-water vehicles.

Thus, the apparently inescapable tendency, whenever more space is needed, is to lengthen out the submarine with a cylindrical section that is simple to make and doesn't disturb the drag of the submarine much. Perhaps, with the same power, it only loses a knot or two. At speed, however, the water rolls back over that cylindrical section more turbulently and more noisily than it would over the more curved shape of a perfectly streamlined hull.

A not inappropriate reference at this point is the history of the *Albacore* and what happened to its descendants. The *Albacore,* whose hull was laid down about half a year before that of the *Nautilus,* became the U.S. Navy's experimental submarine in low-drag shapes and all that these entail in control and hydrodynamic problems. This submarine never carried armament and is driven by a diesel-electric system, good enough to deliver all the data necessary. The *Albacore* demonstrated how advantageous a beautifully streamlined hull could be to a submerged submarine (and how wet, balky, and unsteady it made her on the surface).

The *Albacore* served as a model for the Skipjack class. Succeeding designs—the Permit class, the Sturgeon class, and the Narwhal class—have become successively larger by adding and then increasing the length of a cylindrical midsection. One reason for the increase in size is that these later classes carry large, indeed enormous sonars.

As long as nuclear propulsion plants are extremely expensive and do not change their price much with size, it may be appropriate to give each platform as much sonar range as possible. Yet two 2,500-ton submarines, each with a crew of seventy-five men, would seem far more effective militarily than one 5,000-ton submarine with a crew of 150 men. Can any of the various nuclear nations now build a first-class 2,500-ton nuclear submarine? The one who does it first will have a significant leg up.

As submarines go deeper, the hull will become the most important single item of weight. Although there are dissenting views, most submarine officers believe it is as desirable for a military submarine to achieve greater depths as it is for a bombing plane to achieve greater altitudes. The submarine's susceptibility to detection varies in a complicated way with its maximum operating depth. It achieves a great advance merely by submerging a few inches below the surface. Then it can no longer be detected by radar or, except in certain lighting situations, by eye. As it goes deeper it becomes increasingly hard to detect by surface sonar. Magnetic means of detection become ineffective. Sonars deep in the water mass can continue to detect the submarine even when it is deep, although depth alone reduces its noise somewhat. If, in deep water, a submarine sits down on the bottom, it is virtually undetectable except by the sporadic noises it may make accidentally—by blowing a tank, running a pump, or slamming a hatch shut. A submarine that could operate at, say, 4,000 feet, could transit to many of its patrol areas without getting more than a few feet off the bottom. Such a vessel would present as tough a problem, probably a tougher one, to an active sonar as does a plane flying "on the deck" to a radar.

A deep-diving military submarine faces a number of problems absent in its research cousin. The latter need not carry weapons, let alone the sensors and computers to fire them. A research submarine with a support ship close at hand and with no requirement that it must crash dive at a moment's notice, can return to the surface by dropping a weight. No method could be simpler, even if, for a large submarine, it gets to be a bit expensive. But a military submarine must have some way—gas generators, cryogenic fluids, extremely high-pressure air—for blowing its tanks at maximum depth. Certainly it could drop a weight the first time it wanted to come to the surface. But after diving again, what would it do for an encore?

In the air, relentless pressures developed to make military planes fly faster and higher. With regard to speed, the submarine faces a far more complex problem than does the aircraft. At shallow depth, a submarine could not go faster than about sixty knots without encountering heavy cavitation, great noise output, and a sharp increase in drag. It could evade the cavitation limit only to a degree and only by going deeper. A submarine faces far more drastic penalties if its control in depth is lost or even coarsened by high speed. If the submarine climbs above its set depth, it can broach into the air, an embarrassment at best and a disaster if surface ships are hunting it. If it grazes the bottom it is finished. A submarine running over a continental shelf or in one of the world's numerous shallow seas must stay in a film of water that is at most twenty times thicker than its own diameter. A plane, by contrast, has thousands, and indeed scores of thousands, of feet of leeway.

No submarines yet built can approach sixty or even fifty knots. Additional speed to these levels, assuming they could be obtained without monstrous increases in the size of their engine rooms, would be useful in emergencies, as in evading a torpedo. Otherwise, military submarines are somewhat like lions, who can run very fast indeed but who exert their full speed for a minute or two at a time only once every day or two.

Although current submarine speeds may be adequate, greater depth capability appears to be desirable. The pressure to design deeper-diving submarines may be less on the U.S. Navy than on other navies because of the current overall technical superiority of American submarine technology. However, were other nations to achieve equality in performance or superior ASW capability, the race for the bottom would undoubtedly be on. There remain many opportunities for submarine performance to improve. A combination of the hydrodynamic fineness of the *Albacore,* the depth capability being opened up by new materials, the use of nuclear power plants of lower weight per horsepower, and the full application of today's digitized, microminiaturized electronics can produce a submarine that will give the world's surface navies (of which the United States is first) not just a headache but a fatal disease.

The disease may be in full course even without such developments. Prior to the nuclear era, one of the silent but powerful factors that led to the building of military submarines was what was later to be called their cost effective-

ness. In World War I, a handful of German submarines on
station drove the British Grand Fleet from a good part of the
North Sea, forced merchant shipping into convoy, and kept
hundreds of minesweepers and destroyers busy. In that war,
the Germans deployed 371 U-boats and lost 178 of them
and over 5,000 men. But they sank 5,708 ships, a quarter of
the world's tonnage, and with them an enormous toll of
sailors and troops.

In World War II, the United States deployed about 290
submarines in the Pacific. With 2 percent of the American
forces in the Pacific, these submarines contributed at least as
much as, if not more than, the vast amphibious landings and
the carrier battles to the downfall of the Japanese empire.
The German U-boat effort, although it did not bring victory,
extracted from the Allies a countereffort perhaps ten times
greater. These were vehicles that could barely get below the
ocean's surface and could barely make six knots as they
attempted to escape a charging destroyer. What is the submarine's potential now, as the world skirmishes before
Armageddon?

The True Atlantis

*Men have died, and worms have eaten them, but not
for love.*   —As You Like It, Act IV, Sc. 1

DependING ONLY on the air in his lungs, a man (better
still a woman, since she is physiologically more able to en-
dure the cold and stresses of skin diving) can descend to
perhaps eighty feet. He (or she) can stay underwater for
little more than two minutes. With great exertion, an exceptionally vigorous diver can get below one hundred feet. The
record as of 1967 for a man stripped of face mask, swimming fins, and breathing equipment was 212 feet.* It was
basically a stunt by an extremely experienced individual.
Total time for the dive, surface to surface, was two minutes
six seconds. Working time at depth: zero.

The big 900-pound Weddell seals of the Antarctic have
been tracked down to more than 1,400 feet where they can
stay for a good fraction of an hour. Sperm whales can dive
deeper and longer. And they can come up fast without experiencing the bends—decompression sickness.

For a man, skin diving is a hard and dangerous pursuit
that gives him frustratingly little time on the bottom. Blind,
numb with cold, he can grope about, pull or push ineffec-

* 240 feet in 1968.

tively, and bring up precious little in the way of weight. His limitations were well recognized by the time men had learned to write. By the third century B.C., the island of Rhodes had provided by law that a diver recovering valuables from a depth of sixteen cubits (twenty-four feet) or more was entitled to half their value. In shallower water his share could be as little as one-tenth.

Until the reign of James II the British law was more laissez faire: a tenth for the royal treasury, regardless of depth. But tales about the fortunes being taken from Spanish wrecks (a few of them actually true) grew so notorious that King James' cupidity was aroused. He demanded half of all valuables taken from the sea. Divers are a secretive lot, however, and it is doubtful if he got enough to pay for the time of his investigators and enforcers.

In spite of dangers and hardship, tens of thousands of men and women have been diving for millennia. Except for the diving bell, practical aids to extend their time on the bottom or to improve their effectiveness were absent until about 150 years ago. In the last twenty years progress has been so extraordinary that it is creating, in effect, a new industry.

In the past, as now, divers have brought up food, sponges, pearls, and, occasionally, treasure. They have helped with underwater construction projects, and on occasion, though far less frequently than now, they have fought underwater. The early written history of the Mediterranean contains a number of specific references to military feats of Greek, Trojan, and Phoenician divers. Some were as significant in their more limited circumstances as were the much wider activities of Italian and British divers in this same theater of war 2,000 years later.

In the sixteenth and seventeenth centuries, when Spanish

galleons came to grief on the innumerable lee shores of the Caribbean, the conquistadors sent Indian divers to such wrecks as could be located in shallow water. Enough was recovered to make pickings for today's divers leaner by many millions of dollars. Actually it was first come, first served, for British seamen and assorted citizenry from the Caribbean islands participated enthusiastically and without waiting for an invitation from the Spanish whenever the opportunity occurred.

William Phipps (or Phips), almost as early a down-east Yankee as ever was (born in Maine in 1651), learned enough about these wrecks as he traded in the Caribbean to persuade Charles II to finance him in a hunt for Spanish treasure. He tried the Bahamas and did very poorly for the King's treasury. But he learned of some Spanish ships that had been lost in 1642 on the north short of Hispaniola (now the Dominican Republic). In a later expedition, bankrolled by the Duke of Albemarle and a few of his cronies, Phipps located one of these wrecks. His divers brought up twenty-seven tons of gold and silver, worth then the fabulous amount of £300,000. Albemarle and his friends got most of the money, but Phipps was knighted and later became the first royal governor of the Massachusetts Bay Colony.

Perhaps the most direct link between the past and the present of diving are the 30,000 diving women of Korea and Japan. For at least 1,500 years, generation after generation of women have been foraging for pearls, shellfish, and edible seaweeds in water up to eighty feet deep. Today their only mechanical aids are goggles or face masks. It speaks for the universal intelligence of mankind that these women (as have other groups of unlearned and isolated divers) long ago settled on an efficient cycle of dives and resting periods. In effect, they have a diving table. This is the name for the formal set of instructions, devised in Western countries with the aid of physicians and test chambers, that tells a diver who wishes to go to any given depth how much time he should take to descend, how much time he should spend on the bottom, how slowly he should come up, how long a period, if any, he must spend in a decompression chamber, and how many dives he can take in a day.

Were these divers of the Far East to adopt scuba gear and rubber suits, the present harvest could be gathered by approximately a tenth of the people now at work. Needless to say (or is it fortunately?), the small seaside communities in which most of these women live are fiercely opposed to, and have in some cases outlawed, the use of such equipment. The writer is reminded of a conversation with the director of one of the U.S. Navy's laboratories, who was telling of a large British sonar installed off the coast of England to locate schools of fish, sometimes scores of miles away. The data could then be relayed via radiotelephone to the nearest trawler. His information was that it was working very well, and he added (facetiously, no doubt), "I guess that's the beginning of the end for the fish population around the British Isles."

Interest in diving as a technique to augment local food sources and to recover valuable objects lost on the ocean bottom remains strong. Diving for sport is sufficiently feasible and exciting that millions of adherents around the world indulge. Military diving is now a significant factor in every conflict fought near oceans or large rivers. The main emphasis, however, and the area of most rapid growth is commercial diving, in connection with the offshore oil industry, with underwater construction, and with salvage. Although small in absolute terms, commercial diving is today one of the most rapidly growing industries in the United States. Estimates have been made that the need for professional divers may increase by twenty times in the next decade.

Diving is a difficult field to characterize in terms of what it does, because it does so many and diverse things and is constantly finding new uses. Some branches of marine biology can be investigated in no other way. The scientist-diver has given body, substance, and vitality to the geology of the shallow seas. Most large police departments now have at least one experienced scuba diver. Marine archaeology has become a specialty, with its own textbooks and procedures. Sending down divers to check the soundness of the welds on oil-well rigs and other ocean platforms has become a routine maintenance procedure. With insurance rates what they are, it is an economic necessity.

When the *Daniel J. Morrell* broke up and sank in Lake Huron in November 1966 with loss of almost the entire crew, divers were sent down to report on the condition of the lifeboats, to obtain samples of the hull plates (the ship was nearly sixty years old), and to supply other facts for the Coast Guard investigation. Divers are now sent down routinely to reveal the circumstances of the tragedy whenever a ship sinks to an accessible bottom. Such losses are almost invariably followed by litigation. Divers have therefore become an inevitable adjunct to investigation by coast guards and admiralty lawyers.

The needs to learn the condition of a wreck or of its instruments, to recover a safe or some other specific object, to assess the possibility of salvage for the underwriters, and to break up a wreck because it is an obstacle to navigation have always existed. New needs continue to crop up in unsuspected forms. Some months after the tanker *Torrey Canyon* impaled herself on the Seven Stones Reef and spilled her immense cargo of crude oil to pollute hundreds of miles of beaches in England and France, the appearance of heavy oil slicks off the United States focused attention on the more than hundred tankers sunk off the United States during World War II. The Coast Guard promptly sent divers down to inspect several of these wrecks, one of which, after a quarter of a century on the bottom, was still slowly seeping oil.

No experience on land can condition a man to the feel and appearance of a sunken ship. What it is like can be sensed in the words of Joseph Karneke, for many years a U.S. Navy diver, from a case history in his description of the *West Virginia*, a battleship sunk at Pearl Harbor. He also illustrates, as no landlubber can, the world in which the hard-hat diver works. The Navy wanted to know the extent of damage to the ship, as it rested on the bottom of Pearl Harbor. As Karneke slid down the port side of the vessel, he writes:

All at once, as I slid down her steel skin amidships, there was no more side to her; I was dangling in space . . . In the darkness I held out my arms in the direction the ship should be. There was nothing. I took a few steps in the same direction—still nothing. When I had gone far past the point where the side of the ship would have to begin if it was there, I called topside, asking if I was headed the right way. "I can't find the ship," I explained, silly as it sounded to be saying that you couldn't find a 33,000 ton battle ship that had been under your backside a moment before.

"You're headed all right," said the phone man. "Your bubbles disappeared inside the ship."

It dawned on me that there was a big hole in the side of the vessel, and that I had walked through it without knowing it.

Finally he determined how big the gap was by groping along the jagged edges of steel. "If this was all hole, it was enormous—far bigger than the thirty feet or so ordinarily ripped out by a torpedo." The hole was 105 feet long and thirty-five feet high, made by five torpedoes that Japanese pilots had dropped with almost chain-stitch spacing.

It is a well-known rule of thumb that a pound of explosive underwater can do about four times as much damage as a pound of explosive in air. This interesting little relationship between ships and TNT is a foundation stone in the success of the submarine torpedo. Furthermore, since divers can sometimes go where torpedoes, let alone planes or submarines cannot, saboteurs in diving gear can be highly cost-effective, as the Pentagon would say.

The modern era in military diving can be dated from the sinking of the Austrian ship *Viribus Unitus* by an Italian surface swimmer in 1918. This feat, carried out with virtually no equipment, led to an investigation in the 1920s by the Italian Navy on the possibilities open to scuba-equipped divers transported in midget submarines. No, Agent 007 did not invent this technique for the supercolossal underwater scenes in *Thunderball*.

Because of the great difficulties that then faced the construction of small submarines, the technique finally adopted by the Italians was to have the scuba-equipped divers ride torpedoes at chin-level depth. The pilots submerged completely upon sighting the target ship, attached the torpedo warhead to the target, and then escaped by whatever means they could. It was a technique adapted to the attack of anchored ships and to the short distances and generally calm waters of the Mediterranean.

When this plan was applied in World War II, it was at the beginning beset by equipment failures in the torpedoes and in the diving gear. Eventually, the Italians sunk about 150,000 tons of shipping in this manner. They also drove the English, under the prodding of an outraged Winston Churchill, to emulate them. The British tried to sink the *Tirpitz* in the harbor of Trondheim in this manner. Again, failures in equipment stopped them. Eventually, however, British frogmen in their torpedo chariots sank half a dozen Italian ships.

The British appear to be the first to combine divers with small submarines and thus to start the symbiosis between submarines and divers that is one of the more intriguing trends of current ocean technology. One man of the four- or five-man crew of their X-craft was scuba equipped. The X-craft were thirty-five-ton submarines about fifty feet long that had to be towed close to their area of operations (a miserable period for the crew) before they went in under their own power, through steel nets and minefields, to their destination. One chamber in these small craft was a wet-and-dry compartment (called, in Americanese, a lock in–lock out chamber). When not needed by the diver, the spartan Englishmen also used the same chamber for a head (the ship's toilet).

On encountering, say, a steel net across the entrance to a harbor, the diver would enter the wet-and-dry compartment through a watertight hatch. Another hatch above his head (closed) led to the outside. He would struggle into his frogman suit and close the hatch leading into the rest of the submarine. The compartment would be flooded to sea pressure with water from an internal ballast tank, so as not to affect the trim of the submarine. Then he would open the upper hatch and emerge with his tools to attack his problem for the day. When he returned, he went through the procedure in reverse, closing the hatch above him, letting the crew pump out the chamber, then emerging into the submarine amid the grumbling of the crew, for they did not love a wet, cold, and dripping diver in their crowded quarters.

Where their divers mounted on torpedoes had failed, the larger X-craft of the British succeeded in entering the Altenfjord and sinking the *Tirpitz*. X-craft also sank the Japanese cruiser *Takao* in Singapore, sank a floating dock, and (an interesting harbinger of the future, when the ocean floor will be littered with civilian communicating gear and military surveillance devices) cut the underwater cables between Saigon, Hong Kong, and Singapore.

Vietnam, a country with a long coastline, many rivers, and, glory be, warm water has proved a frogman's paradise. Among the more prominent events in a generation of guerrilla warfare was the sinking, by Viet Cong frogmen, of the hydraulic dredge *Jamaica Bay*, the fourth largest of its kind in the world. It was at times customary in the harbors of Vietnam to have divers check the bottom of every merchant ship twice a day, to ensure that no mine or *plastique* had been attached with a time fuse just short enough to give the Viet Cong frogmen time to slip away.

Frogmen of both sides have frequently arisen unseen from the rivers to conduct a quick raid or blow up a building. In the U.S. Navy these underwater commandos are called SEALs (for Sea-Air-Land) and are hand picked from the Navy's underwater demolition teams.

Much the same diving equipment used in warfare has been used just as casually by marine biologists to investigate a zone once virtually closed to them, the area from the low-water mark to about the 200-foot contour. An astonishing number of new kinds of marine life and, more important, vast amounts of data valuable to science and to commercial fisheries, on how the denizens of this zone live with each other, have been revealed in the past generation. Scuba gear has also sharply increased the resolution, that is, the fineness of detail, with which geological features on the ocean floor can be observed and sampled. This accuracy, important to scientific understanding, is also crucial to efficient prospecting for minerals.

For a considerably longer period of time, at least since about 1900, divers have been stumbling across archaeological treasures on the ocean bottom. At first the discoveries were made by chance, but now the hunt is widespread and systematic, aided by submarines as well as divers. It has become clear that for more than 2,000 years, and perhaps for 3,000 to 4,000 years, ships have been sinking in the Mediterranean and in the shallow seas of southeast Asia. Even today, with the assistance of good maps, ocean-spanning aids to navigation, and, above all, reliable power plants independent of the wind, some 200-300 ships go down every year. At a minimum, at least 23,867 ships were sunk between 1902 and 1961.

For the past few centuries, the actual numbers of ships in service have been in the tens of thousands. Evidence is accumulating that, from the earliest eras of written history, an active maritime trade existed, with casualty rates far higher than today's. Under the major traffic routes of antiquity, the ocean floors must be littered with thousands upon thousands of wrecks, most of them long buried in sediment with no clues for the casual diver. "The richest museum of antiquities in the world," said Solomon Reinoch in 1928, ". . . lies at the bottom of the eastern Mediterranean."

Be that as it may, there are plenty of wrecks elsewhere.

Certain areas all over the world have long been known as wrecking grounds. In these areas, where a combination of heavy traffic and dangerous lee shores have in some cases been taking a toll of ships since neolithic times, thousands of wrecks have probably accumulated, most of them so utterly decayed that only objects of ceramics, glass, and precious metal remain buried in the bottom sediments as evidence. The statistics accumulated along the eastern coast of North America, where the records of ship sinkings over the past 200 years have been fairly good (or at least not utterly lacking), are indications of what probably exists elsewhere on a much larger scale. Since 1816, at least 674 ships have been destroyed on the shores of two small French-owned islands off Newfoundland: St.-Pierre and Miquelon. Farther out in the Atlantic is Sable Island, a shifting ribbon of sand that has gathered up some 500 ships since 1800. Sable Island likes to be known as the graveyard of the Atlantic, but the title can be disputed by Cape Hatteras, the Bahamas, and several other areas.

What should be the haul for the reefs and sandbanks of southeast Asia over which ships have been sailing for considerably more than 2,000 years? Archaeologists have uncovered evidences of traffic between the pre-Christian Roman empire and India, between post-Christian Rome and China, between India and Malaysia, and between the Han dynasty of China and the areas that are now called Burma, Thailand, and Vietnam.

Contributing to the rate at which these wrecks have accumulated is the fact that, in spite of an enormously larger population and a greatly expanded international trade, the twentieth-century world does not possess many more ships than did many past centuries. Twentieth-century ships are

far, far bigger and they go two or three times faster, so that
the volume moved per ship per year is incomparably greater.
Nevertheless, Holland in the early 1600s, when she was "the
wagoner of all the seas," possessed 10,000 sail and employed
168,000 seamen. About a century later, the British alone
employed 8,000 ships (and lost hundreds every year to the
vicissitudes of war and weather). There were many periods
in World War II when the German U-boats were sinking a
smaller percentage of British shipping than did the French
privateers engaged in the *guerre de course* of the pre-Napo-
leonic era.

The first real find in marine archaeology occurred when a
crew of Greek sponge divers were forced by a storm into the
shelter of the island of Antikythera, near Crete. Since it appeared that they would have to stay there several days, they
decided to put the time to use and dived to 150 feet for
sponges. Instead they found bronze and marble statues—
horses, men, women. The statues were loot, perhaps of the
dictator Sulla, en route from Athens to Rome some year in
the first century B.C. The bronze statues aboard were already
400 years old when they sank. Among the smaller items in
that haul was a badly corroded and deformed lump of
bronze that was recognized a year after it had been depos-
ited in a Greek museum as a mechanism. After fifty years of
study it appears that this object, which contained more than
twenty gears, was part of a mechanical computer that could
predict astronomical events. It is unique, utterly alone—the
one complex mechanical device we know of in the ancient
Greek civilization.

In June 1907 another crew of Greek sponge divers were
working off Mahdia, in Tunisia. Mahdia is now a small and
dusty port. But Caesar once visited it, and over the centuries

fleets from Phoenicia, Carthage, Greece, and Rome anchored there. In 130 feet of water a diver found "a lot of big
guns" on the bottom. They were marble columns, and scattered nearby were bronze and marble statues, drinking
bowls, candelabras, and dozens of other items. The ship that
carried them had also set out from Athens. Was it also part
of Sulla's booty? Did the same storm do in both ships?

The Mahdia expedition of 1908–1911 filled six rooms in
the Bardo Museum in Tunis but did not clean out the wreck.
Some forty years later a group of French divers led by
Jacques-Yves Cousteau decided to give the remains of this
wreck a close look, using the new tools, particularly scuba,
that had been developed in the interim. Their first difficulty
was the standard problem in diver navigation, that of finding
the wreck. They had been given careful bearings and had the
advice of Alfred Merlin, the French archaeologist who had
directed the first salvage effort. Nevertheless, it took six days
to relocate the wreck. Cousteau's group brought up little
new except an opinion that unbreached cargo still lay amidships. However, the incident proved the value of the mobile
diver equipped with scuba in archaeological work and sensi-
tized Cousteau to the significance of this phase of diving.

In 1952 divers in Cousteau's group discovered a wreck in
140 feet of water off Marseilles. It was a huge one—a
10,000-amphora ship, for the merchant vessels of ancient
Greece were not rated by the ton but by the number of 6.5-
gallon wine jugs they could carry. (We talk about 50,000-
barrel tankers today.) Amphoras were the standard packages of the era, holding wine, olives, grain, dyes, or ores, as
the circumstances demanded. This ship contained no art
works and no treasure. Instead, it carried some international
merchandise of the period: pottery and wine. Most of the

cargo and much of the ship were returned to the surface, the rotten wood proving by far the more difficult material to handle.

Careful detective work by the archaeologists determined that the vessels had belonged to a Roman merchant named Marcus Sestius who lived on the island of Delos; that the ship had left Delos about 230 B.C. and had stopped at an Italian port before going on to meet its destiny near a great rock that lies about ten miles off the French coast. The find also demonstrated the vigorous state of Greek shipping of the period: 200 years before the birth of Christ tableware, at least, was mass-produced with the aid of wooden molds and efficiently packed in wooden crates for shipment throughout the known world. So much for progress.

It is sufficiently clear that diving has an interesting past, a dynamic present, and a fascinating future. What is the technological history and which are the current developments that have created this state of affairs?

The first mechanical device of any broad benefit to divers was the diving bell, in use before the time of Christ. In far more complicated form, it is in greater use or at least takes part in a greater variety of diving missions today than ever before. A generic descendant of the barrel in which Alexander the Great is alleged to have made a short test dive is the personnel transfer capsule or submersible decompression chamber that is being used as the key underwater support element in saturation diving. And saturation diving, a product of the 1960s, is the key to efficient work in deep water. Although a cylindrical shape is still faintly discernible, these modern diving bells are embellished by reserve air flasks, telephones, hatches, lights, and sometimes closed-circuit TV.

The advantage of getting the divers to the bottom in a water-free cell are many. Until they are ready to step out on the bottom they can breathe gas delivered from the surface rather than taking it from the meager store on their backs. They are in dry air rather than in icy water, thus conserving their strength for the quarter- or half-hour it takes to get them down. The capsule can stay on the bottom as a refuge. It brings the divers back to the surface pressurized and, therefore, quickly. If they come up unprotected, they must make the ascent in stages, stopping for many minutes at each stage. If the dive is deep, they must go into a decompression chamber either way. For true saturation diving, there are few alternatives. Either the diver retires to a bottom habitat after his work shift or he comes up in a diving bell to a surface-mounted decompression chamber. Neither a bottom habitat nor a decompression chamber is comfortable, but the latter, on the surface, permits better medical attention and a few more amenities.

The hard-hat diver, almost the only kind the prewar world was familiar with, dates as a practical matter from sometime in the 1770s, when the Frenchman Freminet first used a pump on the surface to force air down to a diver wearing a copper helmet. (If one cared to compute by nation the number of significant advances in diving equipment over the years, it is likely that France would come out an easy winner.)

Until World War II the brunt of most commercial diving projects fell on this type of diver. To this day there are certain jobs that he can still do best. Nevertheless, although there will be a place for the hard-hat diver for a long time to come and although he shares many of the same dangers and will benefit almost as much from new developments as will the free diver-swimmer, it is the latter who started the real revolution for man in the sea.

The development of scuba (self-contained underwater breathing apparatus) began with a Brooklyn machinist named Charles Condert in 1832. He died using it in the East River the year he invented it. The claim may be disputed by the French, who can say with some justification that the first important step toward a practical self-contained diving apparatus was made by Rouquayrol and Denayrouse in 1865. Although still requiring a hose from the surface, it placed an automatic demand valve and a small air reservoir on the diver's back. It appears to be the first diving gear to be given wide usage. The French Navy diving manuals of the period indicated experience with it to sixty-six feet (twenty meters); the Austro-Hungarian War Ministry said it could be used to 115 feet.

Jules Verne was sufficiently impressed in 1869, just a few years after it had appeared, to make with his pen an obvious improvement to the Rouquayrol-Denayrouse equipment. He cut the air hose to the surface. Thus was born the diving equipment for Captain Nemo's crew in 20,000 *Leagues Under the Sea*. Said Captain Nemo, "You know as well as I do, Professor, that man can live underwater, providing he carries with him a sufficient supply of breathable air. In submarine works, the workman, clad in an impervious dress, with his head in a metal helmet, receives air from above by means of forcing-pumps and regulators."

Professor Arromax: "That is a diving apparatus."

Nemo: "Just so, but under these conditions the man is not at liberty, he is attached to the pump which sends him air through an India rubber tube, and if we were obliged to be thus held to the *Nautilus,* we could not go far."

The argument for the free diver could not be better put today.

Asian lady divers to the contrary, the rest of the world is applying advances in diving technology to practical problems as rapidly as the techniques are developed, for powerful economic incentives are at work. The most recent example is saturation diving, which was conceived only about 10 years ago, was given its first tests in the sea in 1962, and is already in commercial use. Indeed, the industrial users are competing with government-funded projects in devising new equipment and in setting new depth and endurance records.

In 1925 when the American submarine S-51 was sunk by a collision with the *City of Rome* in 132 feet of water, only six civilian divers could be found on the east coast of the United States who were willing to dive to that depth. The entire U.S. Navy had twenty men who were qualified to dive to more than ninety feet.

Today thousands of divers, on this same east coast, are willing to go to much greater depths. Many of the millions of scuba divers who dive for sport are organized into clubs, some of which have hundreds of members and which occasionally organize excursions to interesting wrecks or reefs. As for the military, every maritime power has hundreds, in some cases, many thousands, of trained scuba and hard-hat divers. Amphibious warfare is almost unthinkable today without divers to reconnoiter the beaches, clear away the obstacles, and harass the enemy's shipping.

To a greater degree than perhaps any one other single development, the phenomenal increase in the use of diving equipment for sport and for commercial purposes is the result of the open-circuit scuba developed by Cousteau and Emil Gagnan in France during World War II. This was the first completely practical diving gear to remove the restrictions on movement imposed by the helmet-hose combination of the hard-hat diver. Thus, after a long and frustrating development, in which many inventors—French, American, British, and German—participated, Captain Nemo's desire for a diving suit that would liberate the diver from a fixed base was achieved.

When a diver using the Cousteau-Gagnan open-circuit scuba feels a need for more air, he breathes more deeply. This slightly lowers the pressure in his mouthpiece and thus opens the demand valve more widely. The used air spills out into the sea with a loud hissing that interferes with telephonic communication and also leaves a visible indication on the surface, which is very useful in tracking the diver in peacetime but a menace to his safety in wartime.

The most fundamental problem of the open-circuit system, however, is that a man uses only a small percentage of the oxygen he inspires into his lungs on a given breath. Under normal conditions, when breathing atmospheric air that contains about 20 percent oxygen, the gases he breathes out contains roughly 16 percent oxygen. The nineteenth-century innovators of scuba were well aware of this and from the beginning made efforts to absorb the carbon dioxide from the exhaled gases, to add make-up oxygen to restore its original content, and to have the diver rebreathe the mixture. His endurance on the limited amount of air he can carry on his back, particularly at great depths, where open-circuit devices are particularly wasteful, would be sharply increased.

Several moderately successful versions of closed-circuit scuba systems exist. They are more complicated, more costly, and less reliable than the open-circuit forms, and they have not yet had wide usage outside the military. As an illustration of the engineering difficulty of the problem, it may be pointed out that carbon dioxide has to date been absorbed by various caustic solutions. Many of these, if exposed to sea water, can produce fumes of extreme danger to the diver. Furthermore, the carbon dioxide content should be held close to the partial pressure it has in the atmosphere. At high pressure this gives the control system very little margin of safety. The problem of controlling oxygen is not much easier. As depth increases, the partial pressure of the oxygen must remain more or less constant, which means that the ratio of oxygen in the now synthetic atmosphere around the diver is reduced to as little as 1 percent of the total mixture. This is enough for properly oxygenating the diver's blood at the high absolute pressure that exists at depth, but confronts present oxygen-measuring equipment with dangerously little scope for error.

Not that the various perils of the closed-circuit systems have prevented their use, particularly when no reasonable alternative exists. In 1880, just after the first closed-circuit scuba became available, a tunnel being built under the Severn River in England was accidentally flooded. In an hour and a half, a diver equipped with this new equipment made his way through the twists, turns, and debris of this tunnel to close a door that enabled the excavation to be dewatered. For that time, the feat was akin to Lindbergh's solo flight across the Atlantic.

Liberating the diver from his various tethers—be they safety lines, air lines (hookahs), or telephone wires—has had major consequences, particularly for scientific and military use. A hard-hat diver, tethered by his air hose and signal lines and weighted down so that he cannot swim, has difficulty in covering an area sixty feet in radius (the length of the standard Navy distance line by which the diver is tied to a marker line). On a hard bottom, in clear water, and with little current, he may be able to search this area with one dive. More likely, repeated dives would be in order. A scuba diver, who can swim at an average speed of about 0.85 knots—barely one statute mile per hour—is far more mobile, not only horizontally, but also vertically. The free diver can and frequently does enter confined and tortuous clefts and tunnels—even the interiors of large wrecks. A "hard hat" does so on peril of fouling his air hose (yet there are innumerable examples of hard hats who have, in defiance of all caution, successfully penetrated the innermost compartments of large ships).

For a given depth, neither can stay down longer than the other or take a shorter decompression time. The hard hat needs a sizable support ship and crew. If the surface waves get too rough for his support group, he has to stop operations also. A free diver needs a buddy, for solo diving is a risky business, but he is more independent of support facilities. For missions requiring stealth or mobility, scuba gear is essential. Unless the scuba diver has some sort of vehicle, he must work in calm water. Currents of a knot or more are too much for him. (Because water is about 840 times denser than air, a current of two knots unbalances a man as much as a sixty-seven mile per hour wind in air.) A hard hat, weighted down with lead, can stand in currents of up to 2.5 knots.

A listing of the basic types of diver equipment cannot avoid mention of the "sleeper" in this race, a little-known type of suit that has a chance of upsetting all the better-known trends of development now in evidence. This is the armored, one-atmosphere suit. The aim in this type of suit is to keep the diver at sea-level pressure, breathing the same composition of gases that exists in the atmosphere. He is thus rid of an enormous physiological problem, and thousands of men who by temperament or physical constitution could not be divers would be able to exercise their skills on the ocean floors.

A "hard" suit must be strong enough to resist the outside pressure, that is, must be as heavy walled as a submarine of the same size. Yet a human being contains innumerable joints in his arms, legs, and, particularly, his hands. Unless this armored suit is flexible, unless pressures across the many sliding surfaces are so perfectly equalized that no undue friction develops, the diver is a prisoner in an iron cage. Although a modern suit of this type is built primarily of stainless steel and weighs about 200 pounds, it is no burden to carry on the bottom. Because it is built to house a "90 percentile man" (English translation: 10 percent of the adult male population are too tall, too short, or too fat to fit), it displaces more than 430 pounds of water. After a 185-pound man has climbed in, he still needs some ballast.

The first recorded attempt to solve this dilemma, by building an articulated armored suit, goes back to at least 1838. This was followed by several progressively more complicated types of flexible armored suits during the nineteenth century and several more during the twentieth. An outgrowth of the suit first designed by Lodner Phillips in 1856 and then redesigned in Germany during World War I was used by the Italian salvagers who pulled $5 million in gold out of the SS *Egypt* in the 1930s. That ship was sunk in 438 feet of water, far beyond the capability of the hard-hat divers of that day, and indeed, almost beyond the practical range of divers today. It was an extraordinarily clumsy device, with many ball- and socket-joints, which must have been a nightmare to maintain. Suitable joints for anything as small as a man's fingers were then impossible. The diver wore two tools, à la Captain Hook, at the extremities of his arms.

Since 1955, efforts have been underway to use such new materials as Teflon, nylon, and neoprene and such new mechanical devices as low-friction rotary seals to create spacesuits for astronauts. These must be reasonably airtight and must permit the man inside to flex his arms and legs without exerting superhuman strength. The suit must elsewhere be rigid, for blowing up a flexible suit with air creates a self-defeating stiffness. Since 1964 basically the same technology has been aimed at the much harder job of creating a diver's rigid but articulated suit.

The pressure differential across an astronaut's suit is about five pounds per square inch. For the diver, the pressure difference in 600 feet of water exceeds 270 pounds per square inch. The astronaut's suit can allow a small amount of leakage, which merely increases the amount of air he needs for a stay of given duration outside his spaceship. The joints in the diver's suit must be tight—period. If this development succeeds, and particularly if it includes a successful glove for the diver's hands, it may really shake up commercial and military diving. This is no suit for the Sunday diver; it will carry a high—in fact a truly astronautic—price. Within one of the companies developing such suits, the section of the suit from shoulder to glove is known as the golden arm.

At the moment, the main area of innovation is saturation diving, probably the most important development in diving since the Cousteau-Gagnan invention of an effective open-circuit scuba. The virtue of saturation diving is that it evades many of the economic consequences of the decompression cycle. Unless he is wearing a one-atmosphere suit, the first problem a diver faces as he descends to the bottom is that he must adjust the internal pressure of his body to that of the surrounding fluid. The body is full of semiclosed-off spaces such as the middle ear, the sinuses, and the pleura, even the marrow of his bones. A healthy man (pardon—person) who has no anatomical abnormalities and changes depth gradually can keep the pressure inside these spaces the same as that outside. As long as this equilibrium is maintained, these areas are secure from damage. The rest of him (her) is made up mostly of watery or fatty tissues that don't seem to suffer more from pressure than the body tissues of a fish. That is, as far as we know. Man has a great deal more nervous tissue than a fish. Mice subjected to pressures equivalent to about 1,500 feet have shown some neurological symptoms that call for more investigation. Men compressed below about 1,000 feet have shown abnormal electroencephalograms and motor coordination problems which disappeared, however, after decompression. The causes are as yet not clear, and may yield, as have other medical difficulties, to further research. But until they do, a cloud hangs over plans for deeper excursions into the sea.

If any part of a diver's body, internal or external, gets sealed off so that pressures are no longer equal, he faces the dreaded "squeeze" that can rupture his eardrums, forcibly fill his internal cavities with blood, or drive his eyes and the soft tissues of his face into his mask. In some terrible cases where a sudden fall or accident has caused a loss of pressure in the helmet of a hard-hat diver, his body has been driven, indeed molded, into the helmet.

When the diver begins his return to the surface, the gases

he is breathing take a long time to saturate his tissues. If he is down only a few minutes, he can come up more quickly than if he is down an hour. After half a day to a day, depending on depth, he is fully saturated. Whether he is partly or fully saturated, the diver beginning his ascent is in a predicament. The gases dissolved in his blood, fat, and other tissues must now escape. If they are to do so without damage, by evaporating from his lungs, the pressure around him must be reduced slowly. If he comes up too fast, the gases emerge as bubbles throughout his body. Pressing on nerves and brain tissue, interfering with blood flow, they can cause excruciating pain and frequently permanent damage.

In conventional diving the deeper a diver went, the shorter a time he could safely stay down. For the diver who has no place to go but up to the surface when he becomes too cold or tired or low on oxygen to continue, half an hour at 250 or 300 feet is a very long time indeed. This trip to the surface, like the landing of an aircraft, can be the most hazardous part of the mission, and the hours he must spend in the decompression chamber afterward (if he has been down too long) represent the most tedious and uneconomic part of his job. As recently as 1966 offshore oil drillers did not consider it practical to operate divers below about 250 feet.

"Practical," of course, is a relative term. In the past, the bulk of commercial diving work has been above 175 feet. An operation of very short duration, like closing an easily located valve, could permit greater depth. An emergency or a military situation where a nation's interest is at stake will also strike a different balance between the likelihood of death and the need for action.

The diving tables indicate, conservatively, how long a

man can safely stay at a given depth and in how many stages he should ascend. But people vary one from another and from day to day. Age, obesity, extreme exertion, the after-effects of alcohol, and other factors influencing a person's physical condition or blood circulation can alter an individual's resistance to the bends, generally for the worse.

One of the great virtues of saturation diving is that it reduces the number of times that a diver must decompress, and thus be exposed to the dangers and economic penalties of this process. A diver is paid by the day, not by the time he spends on the bottom. If, by following the conventional tables, a diver can safely spend fifteen minutes at a given depth, that is what the employer gets in return for his money. As a one-time emergency measure, there may be no choice. If hundreds of man-hours are required, a contractor would look for some other way out or pass up the job. In 1939 it took 640 dives to recover the United States submarine *Squalus* from 240 feet of water. The average working time at depth was less than twenty minutes per dive.

In 1957 Dr. George Bond, who is a captain in the U.S. Navy and a record-holding diver, pointed out that once a diver's body is fully saturated he requires no more decompression time regardless of how long he remains on the bottom. Bond then suggested that means be provided on the bottom, including provisions for food and rest, to permit divers to stay down until they get a job done. At the end of a work shift, the diver would enter an undersea habitat where he could take a hot shower, dry off, get a meal, and go to bed in a reasonably comfortable environment. At the end of the job the divers would be pulled up under pressure, transferred to a decompression chamber, and go through only one decompression cycle.

The concept arose from years of experiments in dry chambers at high pressure. Although the U.S. Navy is this country's and undoubtedly the world's largest employer of divers, Bond's suggestion did not initially trigger a vigorous response. However, the significance of his observation was not lost on Cousteau, a long-time acquaintance and professional colleague of Bond. Cousteau, aware that the successful use of saturation diving would lead to an order of magnitude increase in diver productivity, which in turn might have a revolutionary effect on the exploration of the world's continental shelves, proceeded to prove the validity of the concept. Cousteau put down the first undersea station near Marseilles in September 1962 in the comparatively shallow depth of thirty feet. In 1963 he placed stations in the Red Sea to depths of about ninety feet. Almost simultaneously with Cousteau, Edward A. Link began similar experiments.

In 1964 the U.S. Navy, under the direction of Captain Bond (Papa Topside to his divers), ran the first of its *Sea-Lab* experiments, this one in 193 feet of water off Bermuda.

It can be said for the Navy that, once alerted to the significance of saturation diving, it moved with momentum. *SeaLab I* had a budget of, at most, a few hundred thousand dollars. *SeaLab II*, which in 1965 kept crews of divers down for forty-five days in 210 feet of water off La Jolla, California, had a budget of well over a million dollars. *SeaLab III* is absorbing much greater resources from a wide list of commercial and government laboratories. Nor does this take into account the many ancillary programs aimed at developing diver tools and other equipment. With its worldwide commitments and its need to move divers for long distances, sometimes in hostile water, the Navy is also deeply interested in a wide variety of surface vessels and submarines for transporting and maintaining divers. These efforts are sure to spill over into commercial and scientific diving activities.

Although the commercial concerns now utilizing saturation diving have introduced many cost-reducing features, saturation diving is inherently a large-scale operation. It is rarely employed unless time on the bottom must exceed time in the decompression chamber. Whether the divers' habitat is on the sea floor, inside a submarine, on a surface ship, or solidly on land, large pressure vessels, heavy cranes, a complex personnel transfer capsule, and much other equipment are required.

Regardless of the diving procedure or of the equipment used, diving remains a hazardous profession and a sport in which death can be the penalty for panic, faulty apparatus, contaminated air, or a routine mischance. Scores of accidents, many of them fatal, still occur every year. Many divers get lost. Typical, but with a happier ending than some, is the newspaper report of a skin diver who, alone (when he shouldn't have been), was searching for black coral off Maui, in the Hawaiian Islands. When he came up, he couldn't find his boat. Some twelve hours later, to the astonishment of a family strolling on the beach on Molokai, he came ashore. It was a ten-mile swim, with no company except a school of sharks.

For divers who come up too fast or suffer a sudden equipment failure, the penalty can be death or an emergency run to a decompression chamber. Failure rates for treatment of decompression sickness remain high, in some instances as high as 50 percent. Next to casualties from decompression sickness are those caused by presence of carbon monoxide or hydrocarbons in the air supply. Derangements of the diver's metabolism caused by breathing excessive amounts of oxygen or carbon dioxide are also encountered.

In the Western world particularly, it is not good taste to talk about the economic value of human lives. Lives are priceless, or as Charles J. Hitch calls them, "incommensurables," items whose value cannot be quantified in a generally acceptable way. Yet to an oil company deciding whether or not to drill a well in several hundred feet of water or to a salvage concern debating whether or not to buy the rights to a wreck from an insurance company, the dollar costs of a casualty are clear enough. In the current economy of the United States, a commercial organization that suffers a casualty in "line of duty" and is lucky enough to escape legal difficulties with the survivors takes a loss (whether or not an insurance company acts as a partial buffer) of scores if not hundreds of thousands of dollars.

Although the dangers that arise as the diver descends to higher pressure are well known, their physiological mechanisms are not yet thoroughly understood. Man evolved in an inexhaustible and extraordinary stable atmosphere that consists of 20.94 percent (by volume) oxygen, 79.02 percent nitrogen, and a very critical 0.04 percent carbon dioxide. Only a great metropolis, rimmed by industrial and power plants, clogged with automobiles, and studded with rubbish incinerators, can pollute this atmosphere sufficiently to be readily noticed by a human being unaided by instruments. In his evolution man has never needed, and did not develop, good built-in sensors to tell him if he is getting too little oxygen or too much (which can poison him) or an unusual amount of carbon dioxide (which activates one of the two mechanisms that control his breathing).

To a free diver, every breath must come from a cylinder strapped to his back, metered out to him by an assemblage of valves and tubes whose resistances and frictions he must fight with his chest muscles. He can encounter, from this air supply the dangers of anoxia (lack of oxygen), oxygen poisoning (from too much oxygen), hypercapnia (carbon-dioxide poisoning), carbon-monoxide poisoning, nitrogen (or other gas) narcosis, and decompression sickness.

An outside observer is sometimes in a better position to tell what is happening to a diver than the individual himself. The diver getting into trouble frequently feels euphoric—happy and elated. Among the external signs is skin color. Lack of oxygen (cyanosis) tends to make the skin turn blue. If the red blood cells unite with carbon monoxide instead of oxygen, as they will if it is available, those parts of the body that turn blue in cyanosis—like the lips, nail beds, and parts of the skin—instead turn an unnatural red. These, so to speak, are the colors of death.

Too much oxygen can also cause death. Breathing pure oxygen at more than thirty pounds per square inch of pressure (equivalent to about sixty feet of water) causes epileptic-like convulsions in a few minutes. Breathing pure oxygen at one atmosphere of pressure may create lung lesions in as little as a few hours. Controversy still exists whether an astronaut breathing pure oxygen at low pressure (about five pounds per square inch) will be as safe for long space voyages as one breathing a mixture of oxygen and nitrogen.

Because, except at shallow depths and for short periods, the diver dare not breathe pure oxygen, it must be diluted with some inert gas. Nitrogen, in no way an anesthetic at normal pressure, becomes increasingly narcotic as he descends. With training, some divers can, to a degree, con-

sciously compensate for this narcosis. As with alcohol, however, each man achieves his own level of tolerance. A very
few divers, using oxygen-nitrogen atmospheres, can work
more or less effectively at 150 feet. Below that depth, diluents
other than nitrogen are called for. Krypton is more narcotic
than nitrogen. Xenon is believed to be as narcotic as laughing
gas (nitrous oxide) even at atmospheric pressure.

Neon is less narcotic than nitrogen and impairs voice quality less than helium, but is expensive. Helium has been used
at depths exceeding 900 feet. It is apparently much less narcotic than nitrogen. Hydrogen comes under suspicion as an
explosive hazard whenever it is mixed with an appreciable
quantity of oxygen. However, oxygen ratios below 4 percent,
corresponding to about 190 feet and below, are not considered
explosive. Relatively little work has yet been done with hydrogen.

Helium has been under investigation as an element in synthetic atmospheres since 1924 and was used in diving on the
USS *Squalus* in 1939. It is about as soluble in the water
tissues of the body as is nitrogen but is much less soluble
than nitrogen in the body fats. Although the exact mechanism of gas narcosis is not known, there is speculation that
nitrogen's great solubility in fat (about five times as much as
in water) is associated with its more harmful effects as compared to helium.

The sharpest lesson learned from *SeaLab I* and *II* (or
perhaps relearned, for divers in all but tropic waters have
always suffered from cold) is that unless something radical
is done to reduce the diver's heat loss, the main advantage of
saturation diving—that of allowing a man to work on the
bottom for long periods—is aborted. Today the most frequently encountered limit to diving endurance is not lack of

air but the accumulation by the diver of too great a thermal debt.

Even in *SeaLab I,* whose location was chosen in part because the water, at 68-69°F., was relatively warm, the divers could not stay out for more than an hour or so. In the same temperature near the surface they could have worked several times as long.

It did not take much investigation to find out why. It was not so much that water conducts heat twenty-five times faster than air and that its capacity for absorbing heat is over 1,000 times greater. This is why divers wear long woolen underwear and sponge rubber suits. However, at the 193 feet of the *SeaLab I* experiment, the divers were breathing a mixture of only 4 percent oxygen, 16 percent nitrogen, and 80 percent helium. Helium conducts heat about six or seven times as well as air and is a highly penetrating gas. It quickly filled the porosities in the rubber suits and, by replacing the air, greatly reduced its insulation value. Furthermore, the divers' lungs were also filled with helium under pressure, and this sharply increased the body's loss through the chest walls.

Man is a mammal whose internal temperature is held constant by an intricate series of biologic controls when he is in good health and who becomes extremely uncomfortable and eventually unconscious if this internal temperature goes up or down even a few degrees, so a diver is soon in trouble if the water around him is either too hot or too cold.

Water over 86°F. is too hot to work in for long. A man who is exerting himself strenuously cannot dump enough heat into such an environment to keep his temperature constant. Water above this temperature is found only in a few ocean areas and even there only near the surface. It is a relatively rare problem.

Generally, the oceans are inconveniently cold. The great mass of this planet's ocean water, except near the surface in the lower latitudes, is not much above 40°F., only about 8° F. above the freezing point of fresh water. Even on the continental shelves, water as low in temperature as -2°C. (28.4°F.) can be encountered. The minimal skin temperature for comfort is about 91°F. At a skin temperature of 55°F. nerve damage can result. If the deep body temperature, the so-called core temperature, drops below 86°F., loss of consciousness follows. Centuries of ship wrecks have demonstrated that unprotected men plunged into cold water will begin to die within minutes. The grim rule of thumb is that they die in the order of their weight, the thinnest and smallest first.

A diver trying to keep warm is using energy at a prodigious rate, is burning oxygen in proportion, and is getting as tired as (and more uncomfortable than) if he were working strenuously. If his skin temperature drops below about 83°F. he starts to shiver, sometimes so violently that he cannot hold his breathing mouthpiece between his teeth. Unless he is an Eskimo, his hands start to hurt as his finger temperature drops below 60°F.

A dry suit that traps a layer of air around the diver's body is a step toward proper insulation. However, it must be sufficiently well made and maintained to prevent small leaks from becoming a problem. Conventional dry suits are also bulkier and more apt to fold and pinch the skin than wet suits. The wet suit cannot be increased sufficiently in thickness to completely protect the diver thermally. Particularly around hands, fingers, and feet, an increase in thickness would also decrease mobility. Attention has therefore focused on heated suits. The easiest procedure is to weave fine resistance wires into the suit, à la electric blankets. In really cold water the electrical load can reach one kilowatt of power per hour. Since the aim is at least four hours of protection, the diver must carry around a large battery, a bulky addition to his equipment.

For the astronauts, garments (a sort of underwear) through which hot water is circulated in thin tubing have been developed. Liquid-heated garments are also being considered for divers. From the point of view of weight and bulk, a radioisotope generator is the most practical heat source, if the diver is not to be tethered to a hot-water source. Because the diver must be protected against harmful radiation—and he can't go around carrying a few hundred pounds of lead shielding—one of the soft alpha emitters must be used as fuel, such as plutonium 238. The alpha emitters are also the most expensive of the radioisotopes available for power sources. The AEC has been investigating such a power pack for *SeaLab III.*

A successful radioisotope power source for divers would be useful not only to keep them warm but also to power various hand tools. It could spectacularly improve the efficiency of military divers and commercial divers with no access to topside power. But it is not yet for the casual sportsman, unless he is a millionaire. The check-writing pen of the scuba diver of ordinary means would automatically go hard astern when confronted with the sales slip for such an item.

Adequate thermal protection for the diver becomes more critical as the diver's breathing apparatus becomes more efficient. Currently few diving rigs carry enough air for more than one or two hours work at depth. If the diver encounters a condition under which he can work longer, he must use a hookah or get his air supply renewed at an underwater habitat. Increasingly, commercial divers are solving the air supply, thermal, and communication problems by tying the diver to a personnel capsule on the bottom with air hoses, hot water pipes and telephone lines, thus giving up mobility for endurance.

A discussion of the diver's physiological problems is not complete without mentioning an utterly different approach than keeping the diver in a gaseous atmosphere, no matter how exotic its composition. This approach, conceived by Dr. Johannes A. Kylstra, calls for filling the lungs with a fluid that has been saturated with enough oxygen to keep a mammal alive. Ordinarily, water at sea level contains no more oxygen per cubic foot than the atmosphere at an altitude of about 70,000 feet. In order to dissolve enough oxygen into the water, some eight atmospheres of pressure (about 117 pounds per square inch) is required. This method seems most appropriate, therefore, for depths below about 250 feet. Gases that could cause narcosis or would lengthen the decompression time can be excluded from the solution.

One of Kylstra's interests is to permit a human being to withstand the enormous accelerations that would be convenient (or unavoidable) in spaceships designed for long interplanetary voyages. A fetus floating in the amniotic fluid of the uterus, with all its internal voids filled with this same fluid, is itself immune to accelerations hundreds of time greater than those that can kill its mother. Similarly, an astronaut, with his lungs and other air spaces temporarily flooded, and floating weightlessly in a fluid-filled container, could survive phenomenal shocks.

The procedure looks tempting to divers, too, for it would eliminate many of the problems they face because of the great pressures in the deep sea. However, neither man nor for that matter porpoise can survive for long with his lungs filled with just any old fluid, let alone pure water. The lungs are a permeable membrane of extensive area. If they are filled with a liquid at all unlike the complex composition of their own blood and body fluids, dissolved materials will start to move across this membrane by osmosis. Aside from the possibility of damage to the lung tissue, changes in the volume and the chemical content of the body fluids can quickly produce very dangerous, and eventually fatal, results.

Although the diver can now get enough oxygen by inhaling and exhaling a sufficient volume of this pressurized solution, he must also rid himself of the carbon dioxide he is constantly generating. With fluid filling the lungs, this is proving far more of a problem than getting enough oxygen. Ocean mammals, like seals and porpoises, have an internal chemistry that temporarily permits their bodies to accumulate quite an overload of carbon dioxide. Man is not that versatile. Chemicals are available that, when added to the breathing liquid, can ameliorate this condition, but only to a degree.

Because water weighs some 840 times more than air at sea level, and because it takes far more effort to handle a given volume of water than an equal volume of air, the work the lung muscles must do in order to move adequate amounts of liquid in and out of the lungs is scores of times greater than when breathing air. Kylstra suggests that mechanical assistance be provided. Other and more complex differences exist between fluids and air as a medium for transferring gases across biological membranes. One is the very much slower rate, thousands of times slower in fact, at which oxygen and carbon dioxide diffuse through water. Even the mechanical structure of the lung membrane must be different. It is believed that one reason why fish suffocate when out of water, in spite of the much richer source of oxygen available, is that their gills, a series of plate-like structures optimized to extract dissolved gases from a relatively dense liquid, tend to collapse in air and thus drastically reduce the area available for gas transfer. Nor are the millions of tiny sacs, the alveoli, at the terminals of the bronchi in the mammalian lung, optimally constructed to extract oxygen from, or dump carbon dioxide into, a liquid.

In the many millions of years since such mammals as seals and whales returned to the sea, not one has attempted to retrace the path to the fish's methods of breathing. The inadequate amount of oxygen in the water for the vigorous existence of a mammal, the difficulty in getting rid of carbon dioxide, and the heavy work required for breathing are undoubtedly among the chief reasons.

However, since 1961, when experiments with mice first occurred at the University of Leiden, in the Netherlands, scores of animals, most of them mice but many of them dogs, have lived, sometimes for many hours at a time, with their lungs full of oxygenated fluid. Although resuscitation —if that is the word to describe draining the saline solution from the lungs and restoring the animals to a state of normal breathing in air—has presented problems, a high percentage of the animals have survived.

It is a daring and ingenious concept that can be successfully explored only by a profound understanding of the
human body and by meticulous procedure. If it succeeds,
liquid breathing will be another path for the entrance of the
diver into the deep reaches of the sea.

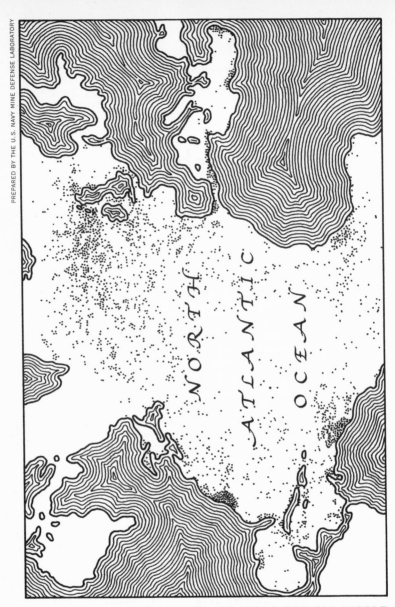

PREPARED BY THE U.S. NAVY MINE DEFENSE LABORATORY

SHIPS SUNK IN THE NORTH ATLANTIC DURING WORLD
WAR II BY GERMAN SUBMARINES
(EACH DOT REPRESENTS ONE SUNKEN SHIP)

For well over 2,000 years ships of several hundred tons and more have
been coursing the high seas. Hundreds of thousands now litter the floors
of the ocean—the results of storm, negligence, and war. Over 10,000
ships were sunk during World War I and II alone. The dots on the
above map represent the hulls sent to the bottom by one belligerent in
one war in one ocean area.

Ocean Robots

I can understand how someone might think it wasn't worth the money to send people up there [to the moon]. But any scientist who says that it has no scientific value is—and you can quote me—a fully paid-up, card-carrying moron. Can you imagine Darwin's discovering the theory of evolution if all he saw sent back from the voyage of the Beagle were a few blurred television pictures?

 —ARTHUR C. CLARKE, during an interview prior to his delivery of the keynote address at the Fifth Goddard Memorial Symposium

Because of the restricted bottom search time of manned vehicles, further exploitation of the unmanned vehicle for search and recovery is recommended. Attractive features of the unmanned vehicle are potentially an order of magnitude increase of bottom time and immunity from concern over operator safety.

 —Recommendation from the executive summary of the final report prepared for the secretary of the Navy and the chief of naval operations on the search and recovery of the H-bomb off the Spanish coast

CONSIDER A TIRED BUSINESSMAN after a hard day with his accountant. He has repaired to a night club to restore his soul. Morosely he lifts a martini to his lips, his little finger, complete with large diamond ring, daintily extended. His mind, otherwise occupied, ignores the fact that this minor maneuver employs scores of muscles, each with intricate feedback loops to nerve endings and brain.* He casts a

---

* The hand of man, whether engaged in swinging a baseball bat or carving a David out of a block of marble, remains the supreme tool of this

bloodshot eye at the stage, and the image of a chanteuse or, if he is lucky, a singing ecdysiast, forms on the millions of rods and cones that line his retinas. While not dismissing this enchanting image from his mind, he simultaneously continues to meditate on his profit and loss statement with a corner of his brain, that is, with only a billion or so of the scores of billions of neurons in his inventory.

Modern technology can build some rather complicated robots, but not with this kind of profligacy in components. At the moment of this writing one of the more spectacular examples are the Surveyor probes, each of which must survive a journey to the Moon. Then, in a sequence of exact measurements and intricately sequenced braking operations, it sits down safely on the Moon's surface and proceeds, on command from a man stationed a quarter of a million miles away, to dig, measure, and test in a parody of a scientist in action. The robot has arms of sorts, manipulators that can reach out, bend, and even rotate—something that a mechanic with a socket wrench in hand would dearly love to emulate. A complicated manipulator can have in the order of ten servomechanisms and several joints.

To compare a hand with a manipulator, or worse still, to compare the human brain with the sensing and computing systems that control the manipulator, is to court falling into a series of logical traps. They are not of the same class. Logic to the contrary, however, efforts to choose between them cannot be avoided, for, increasingly, machines are taking over some of the more repetitive and dangerous tasks once performed manually.

---

universe. So complex is the anatomy of the hand that to this day some confusion remains as to the exact number of muscles and nerves that operate the fingers. Repair of the hand is a highly specialized field of surgery.

Economics and expediency demand, in more and more cases, that some ad hoc choice be made between man and machine according to the special compulsions of the particular problem. Those of the undersea world still tend to be very much in the exploratory stage. Repetitive tasks such as characterize large-scale industry are still few and far between.

A robot, according to the dictionary, is a machine devised to function in place of a living agent. You are not required to pay a robot wages. If you cry when the robot is lost, injured, or destroyed, it is because your pocketbook hurts, not your heart. It's just as well. Oceanographers have had periods when half the "pop-up" devices they sent down to the bottom failed to pop up.

If one wants to explore an environment inaccessible to man, the use of a probe or robot, however simple, is inescapable. Centuries ago, an occasional shipmaster, approaching a familiar landfall, would throw over a sounding line with a little tallow on the bottom of the weight. When it was hauled up, the few grains of sand or mud adhering would indicate the kind of bottom under the ship. To that rare skipper with an exceptional memory and much experience, this would sometimes yield a clue to his position.

When, in the 1870s, the scientists on the *Challenger* wanted samples of the deep-ocean floors, they sent down trawls, many of which would snag on obstructions and be lost, and gratefully examine the few scrapings brought up.

Today, the devices that can be dangled at the end of a long line are more versatile. They can dig cores twenty feet long, scan the bottom with sonar or closed-circuit TV, measure magnetic fields, take bites out of the bottom with accompanying photographs, measure temperature and pressures, and perform dozens of other relatively simple, preprogramed actions.

When manipulator arms are mounted on the structure that is sent down, a still wider series of possibilities are opened up. A man stationed more or less comfortably aboard the ship can watch what is going on through the robot's Cyclopean TV eye and guide the mechanical hands just as if he were there—or so it reads in the specification sheet. There remains an enormous gap between eyes and TV cameras, of which the limited resolution of the camera—its sharpness of sight—is only one aspect. (Who would volunteer to be operated on by a robot guided by a surgeon watching a TV screen?)

Underwater robots can be divided into either reconnaissance forms that scan, measure, and survey or into machines that do something to the environment—like picking up a piece of pipe or closing a valve. The difference between the two types is almost invariably a mechanical hand—a manipulator. This is increasingly standard equipment on manned vehicles, also. The function of a manipulator in the ocean is precisely what it is in the area that spawned them, the hot labs of the nuclear-energy installations. Barred from handling anything that was radioactive, or "hot," technicians had to back off behind a lead or concrete shield and do their job remotely. It was natural that these remote-control devices would attract the attention of the designers of research submarines, who must put inches of steel between the pilots and the underwater world they see just outside their windows, and of the designers of underwater robots, whose operators must sit in a ship at skyscraper heights above the bottom.

One might call any remotely controlled device—even a

hoist—a manipulator, but by common understanding the term is reserved for machines that can operate something like a human hand. The kinds that are now available, from the relatively few manufacturers who have succeeded in this difficult field, are called either master-slave manipulators or powered manipulators. The former will repeat, like a three-dimensional pantograph, every action of the operator. Whatever motion or force he supplies to the control handle is quite accurately transferred to the working end on the other side of the protective barrier. Likewise, any resistance the tongs meet is transferred back to the operator's hands. This kind of manipulator cannot push or pull more strongly than the operator. If he wants the device to move three feet to the right, so must he. If he gets tired, so in effect does the manipulator. In versatility and delicacy of control these master-slave manipulators are as yet unmatched.

They are not used underwater. A man in the tiny control cubicle of a research submarine does not have the room to move about as freely as he must with a master-slave manipulator. At least as great a difficulty is the virtual impossibility of sealing off the many rods and cables that, with this device, must pass through the submarine's hull.

All the manipulators so far mounted in submarines or underwater robots are servopowered. The field of coverage of the arm is now independent of the amount of room the operator has. A large unit would have, in the terminology of crane operators, a maximum outreach of perhaps fifteen feet and at that distance could lift about 500 pounds. Only an electrical control cable, relatively easy to seal against water leakage, need pass through the pressure hull. The operator can do his viewing by eye or by TV camera, which, quite conveniently, can be mounted on the manipulator itself so that it can be moved at will into the best position for seeing.

None of the manipulators developed for land use can be used "as is" on a submarine. Materials more or less impervious to salt water must be chosen; the control wires and hydraulic lines casually strung on the outside of land manipulators must be tucked out of the way of wave action, or they will soon be ripped off. Because it is impossible to seal the many joints of a manipulator unless the pressure inside is as high or preferably slightly higher than the pressure outside, some kind of compensating bellows must be added. The result is that the loss of a manipulator arm from a submarine can be as costly as totally wrecking two or three Rolls-Royces.

The first manipulator arm to be mounted on an underwater device went abroad RUM, (Remote Underwater Manipulator). About six months later, in 1961, a manipulator was first mounted on the bathyscaph *Trieste*.

Pilots of manned submarines have a strong aversion to carrying any protuberance that might snag on the bottom. Pilots have strongly and repeatedly objected to any scheme in which they are winched down to a spot on the bottom, such as the hatch of a sunken submarine. They fear the possibility of being snarled in the wire. A manipulator arm, in a parody of a human arm, can have the equivalent of a shoulder, an elbow, a wrist, and even a finger or two, all of which offer some potential for trouble. If it grabs hold of something on the bottom, or vice versa, and can't let go, the submarine is pretty well anchored. *Alvin,* for example, cannot pull with more than about a hundred pounds force and can be rolled about, as it has, by the attacks of a swordfish. The pilots, therefore, insist that they be able to jettison the manipulator at will. In the early designs that capability was all too obviously there. At least two manipulators have inadvertently received the "deep six."

Manipulators nevertheless have become *de rigueur* on undersea craft. Some work boats are designed to carry as many as four arms, all of them capable of being neatly tucked against the hull when not in use so that they are less likely to be scraped off by waves, ocean bottom, or encounters with the support ships.

Manipulators, guided of course by people, have demonstrated that they can drill holes underwater, cut away obstructions, place explosive charges, tie knots, dig away sand, and in general do just about everything for which tools and adequate direction can be provided. Unlike a human being, who must make do with his wrist and fingers, a manipulator can mount a variety of tools—a small, more or less delicate gripper or a big claw that is capable of grabbing a torpedo. Many manipulators are supplied with an entire rack of power tools and can pick up wrenches, stud drivers, water-jet pumps, or whatever is required (and available) to suit the occasion. But a manipulator can't improvise, nor can it play a Beethoven sonata on the piano, even with Emil Gilels at the controls.

Since a manipulator is a sort of servopower substitute for a man's arm, it is not much of an extension in concept to visualize similar substitutes for the rest of his body. One such device already in the laboratory is the exoskeleton, a powered metal frame around a man that responds with amplified force to each movement of his limbs and body. A stevedore so equipped can stride around the docks carrying thousand-pound loads. Exoskeletons appear particularly appealing for divers, who are generally severely handicapped in the useful forces their own muscles can produce. Nor does the exoskeleton necessarily have to look like a human frame. It can look like a surrealistic horse, and in fact such all-mechanical horses have been built. In announcing that it was soliciting a bid from a major manufacturer to build one of these gadgets, the United States government referred to it as an "ambulating quadruped."

At the moment, such exoskeletons and striding vehicles are very much in the development stage. They have yet to prove their practicability, a matter primarily of demonstrating some economic or functional advantage over existing devices.

The ideal robot, of course, does not need a man close by to guide it. But the more independent it is, the more expensive and complex. The dilemma in ocean engineering arises from the fact that a man can generally be put just where the robot is—either by use of a submarine, from which the operator still cannot get his hands directly on the work, or, at a shallower depth, in a diver's suit. It costs a great deal of money to do this; the pilot or the diver gets tired after four to eight hours and generally won't work at all at night; and there is likely to be an investigation if anything goes seriously wrong. On the other hand, the man on the scene knows in far greater detail and from a wider variety of senses what is going on than the observer limited to a TV screen. If it is too muddy to see, he can feel. And the man, weaker than the machine, uncomfortable, and perhaps gripped by fear, can improvise in emergencies. The automatic devices shine where there is a very carefully prepared work program, with virtually nothing deviating from schedule, and where the environment in which the job is done is exactly as expected by the designer.

The same generalities hold in the space program, though they are occasionally obscured by issues of national prestige.

After great expenditure the space robots have accomplished wonders. They have flown past Venus and Mars and have safely landed on the Moon. With enormous expense men can be sent to the Moon and, perhaps, with still more massive funding and with far greater risk, to the nearer planets. And, very probably, they will be.

In the sea the balance between applications for robots and for manned vehicles or divers is different than in space because it is generally easier and safer to get the man there. The oceanographers continue to expand the use of these various towed, tethered, and free automatons. They were used to good advantage in the *Thresher* and H-bomb searches. They are becoming almost routine in the recovery of torpedoes, and sometimes in the recovery of more secret devices, from depths down to several thousand feet. They have been used to locate many aircraft wrecks and some ship wrecks, and, to a limited extent, in the offshore oil industry. Robot devices for underwater use now include not only collections of such search devices as cameras, sonars, and magnetometers towed at the end of a line and more complicated tethered devices armed with manipulators. They can also be completely free, selfpowered vehicles that are almost the equivalent of small submarines.

In 1967 towed sonars, magnetometers, and cameras were used exclusively in locating the remains of the *Robert Lewis Stevenson*, a World War II liberty ship off the Aleutian Islands. The reason that the U.S. Navy went to such pains to locate an old hulk is that it had been loaded with 2,000 tons of explosives a few months earlier and deliberately scuttled to explode in deep water and thus simulate the explosion of a small nuclear bomb. Although all sorts of expedients had been taken to make sure the ship sank to the bottom immediately, it drifted, deeply submerged, toward land and sank twenty hours later without detonating. It was essential to conclude this highly embarrassing event either by locating the wreck with sufficient precision to permit marking its position on the maps, by detonating the explosives aboard, or by demonstrating that it was no longer a hazard. Working only from the surface, the USNS *Silas Bent* located the wreck and on the fourth try succeeded in positively identifying it with photography. Specially prepared bombs were dropped on the hulk but failed to detonate the explosives. Although marked on the charts, the *Stevenson* is no longer considered a threat.

Another class of tools are free-fall devices that go only up and down; that is, once dropped overboard they drift down to the bottom, gather their data, and then, either on contact with the ocean floor or after a delay that can extend for months, begin their upward journey. Some of these devices are expendable: they measure and report via acoustic telemetry as they drop down, and that is it.

The number and variety of these unmanned devices is so great, their areas of strength and weakness are so diverse, the potential for new forms so immense that only a few representative forms, will be examined here.

One of the simplest of the automatic devices used by oceanographers is the Swallow float. In the sense of resting on the surface of a fluid, it doesn't really float. Rather, by taking advantage of the small difference in compressibility between liquids and solids, it descends to a depth that can be more or less preselected and stays suspended there while it is taking measurements.

Water, it is said, is incompressible. Not so. To paraphrase Orwell, all materials are compressible but some materials are more compressible than others. For example, most structural metals are less compressible than water. Thus, if one constructs a cylinder of aluminum that is just slightly heavier than water at the surface and throws it overboard, it will sink. As the English oceanographer Dr. John Swallow realized, the cylinder will not necessarily sink until it hits bottom. As the cylinder sinks and grows denser, the water around it is getting heavier at a still faster rate. Eventually, the float becomes just as light as the water around it, and it stops sinking. In this state of neutral buoyancy it can float indefinitely at great depths. Because it can contain batteries and an acoustic pinger, it can be tracked by a surface ship. Thus deep-ocean currents have been traced, and to most oceanographers' surprise, such currents have turned out to be more frequently turbulent and more rapid than had been expected. Nor do they flow in the same direction as the surface currents.

The original Swallow floats contained no means by which they could return to the surface. For cases where the records must be brought back for study, floats have been devised that can drop a weight after a pin holding it in place has dissolved or corroded away or after it has hit the bottom and in this way triggered the release mechanism. Gas can be generated so that the instrument package becomes buoyant, either after receipt of an acoustic command from the surface or by reaching a preset depth.

If small wings are put on a streamlined body that houses a gas generator, it becomes an underwater glider that can make long voyages on very little fuel. As it is thrown overboard, a tank fills with water, which ballasts the glider so that it starts on a long, gentle slope downward. Then at a preset depth a pressure gage actuates the gas generator. Water is blown out of the ballast tank and the device glides upward to start another cycle. Gravity supplies most of the power.

That is an example of a robot with a preset cycle. If, however, the men topside wish to send commands to the robot, they must be connected to it either by a wire or by an acoustic telemetry system. Telemetry means only communication at a distance. Many reliable methods exist, but in the sea, acoustic telemetry is virtually without competition, in spite of some tiresomely complicated restrictions. In the past used only for voice communication (not yet much good, of course, with robots) acoustic telemety was first extended to the sending of very simple coded messages like "blow up." This was addressed, of course, to an explosive link that would initiate some simple action like releasing an instrument from its anchor. Some fairly elaborate systems are now in use.

Unlike radio telemetry, which can reach to the planets, the range of underwater telemetry systems tends to be measured in miles. Such systems are susceptible to difficulties that would take hundreds of pages to describe in detail. This helps to explain the persistence of cables, which however much they reduce the mobility of the robot at least provide a reliable channel through which to transmit power and information.

Under proper conditions a sensor towed by a ship can survey considerably more area per day than can a free submarine. One example is the side-looking sonar which must be towed just above the bottom so that its narrow beam can highlight the various bumps, and throw into shadow the various hollows, of the bottom.

Observers in a small submarine running at a battery-consuming speed of four knots can examine at best an area the size of a generous-size living room in one second. In an hour they might, in exceptionally good conditions, cover about five acres.

If a side-looking sonar is towed by a surface ship at comparable or slower speeds, it can map an area, depending on how small an object it wants to see, from ten to several hundred times larger. It can detect detail that varies in size from perhaps six inches to several feet. However, to discover, as it has, large sections of an airplane wreck, an oil-drill rig overturned in the Gulf of Mexico, or an earthquake fault off Alaska is one thing. To "see" a bomb half-buried in the mud and to distinguish it from an old rubber tire is quite another. Be it man, beast, or mechanism, the smaller the object that has to be found, the slower its search rate. When in a collision with its support ship the *Alvin* lost a manipulator that dropped into 4,400 feet of water, it would have been impractical to hunt for it by eye. But by carefully scanning a two-mile by one-mile area with sonar, *Alvin* found its five-foot arm on its third dive.

Sonars do best when any suspicious object they locate is promptly identified by some other means—by a diver, the submarine's pilot, a TV camera, a magnetic detector. If this kind of partnership, not always easy to establish, is absent, their efficiency as search devices can be sharply reduced.

Rough water or poor visibility interferes with and sometimes prevents the launching of manned submarines. In heavy seas the launching and retrieving of automatic search devices is no picnic either, but greater risks can be taken. Thus, in preliminary searches for large, easily identifiable objects or for dangerous objects like mines, a towed sensor or a sonar coupled with such other sensors as TV cameras and magnetometers is the method of choice.

Companies who want to look at their cables or pipelines tow sleds loaded with lights and TV cameras. If they want to bury the cables so that passing ships will not pull them up with their trawls and anchors, they add instruments for measuring soil strength and the fine detail on bottom topography that depth sounders cannot yet record. And finally they add plows, to create the ditch into which the cable is laid. Launching and retrieving these multiton plows from the deck of a rolling and pitching ship call for some maneuvers that would surely astonish a farmer whose idea of launching a plow is to drag it out of the barn.

A rugged winch is a prerequisite. Towing loads for a device that is pulled over a rough bottom by a surging and heaving ship can show phenomenal variations.

Typical of the tethered robots that have accomplished some fairly complicated tasks under water are MOBOT and CURV. Developed in the early 1960s, MOBOT was constructed for a large oil company primarily to operate on well heads and thus reduce the requirements for divers.

Although MOBOT dangles at the end of its power and communication cable, it is nevertheless equipped with propellers, by which it can swing forward or backward, or can rotate. More recent models have feet with which to stand on the bottom. They can also carry, as required, lights, cameras, sonars, and, of course, various numbers of manipulator arms. To the degree that water conditions permit, these various lights and cameras enable the operator topside to see what is going on and to control the device as if he were on the bottom. An experienced operator ceases to be consciously aware of the mechanics of the situation—that he is sitting perhaps 200 feet above the robot and is looking at some television screens rather than at a well head on the ocean bottom. He soon feels that he is the robot—that its arms are his arms, its blurred vision, his.

It could be argued that a device tied by an apron string of cable to an operator is not truly a robot vehicle. There are,

and have been for years, a large number of free, self-propelled vehicles that are connected to the operator by a
telemetry link or are completely preprogramed. In the past
they have been called torpedoes. The U.S. Navy alone fired
close to 15,000 torpedoes in World War II, and estimates
for their use by all the combatants in that war approach
50,000.

A torpedo or a free-running oceanographic probe (and
there is little difference between them in principle) is the
first complex robot ever made in quantity. Like a small submarine, it needs a streamlined and controllable hull, a power
plant, a guidance and control system, and—in its oceanographic version—a set of instruments or tools with which to
do its job, a means to record or communicate to base the
data it measures, and a recovery system. However, small
unmanned vehicles, trimmed beforehand to almost neutral
buoyancy, do not need a ballast system.

A war torpedo, for example, is generally made several
hundred pounds heavier than its displacement, so that if it
misses its target and eventually runs out of fuel, it will sink
"harmlessly" down to the bottom. Otherwise it becomes a
floating mine, dangerous to friend, foe, or neutral traveler.
As long as it is going fast enough the torpedo need not sink
because of this extra poundage. By raising its nose a few
degrees it gets enough lift from its body and fins to carry
the extra weight.

This practice has been followed almost universally since
1907 when, at a press conference held at The Hague, Sir
Ernest Satow pointed out, "The high seas, gentlemen, are a
great international highway. If in the present state of international law and custom, belligerents are permitted to fight
their battles there, it is nontheless incumbent on them to do

nothing which might, long after their departure from a particular place, render this highway dangerous to neutrals who have an equal right to use it."

In spite of this considerate suggestion, scores of thousands of mines and torpedoes, a small but unknown percentage of them with warheads still intact, now litter the ocean floors. Hardly a year goes by without some fishing net setting one off, with casualties to ships and men. Now that small submarines are beginning to prowl close to the bottom the hazard is increasing. And if no other place than the floor is found for the radioactive wastes from atomic bomb and nuclear power plants, Sir Ernest's dictum takes on an added dimension.

Like on a torpedo, a large submarine, if in a sporting mood, can drive down under power while considerably lighter than its full displacement or can maintain its depth while heavier. But a submersible that must change speed drastically, slow down, or, worse still, hover in a given spot cannot adjust its depth by changing its lift. Lift is a dynamic effect; it varies with the square of speed. Such submersibles must be able to change their buoyancy and to move their centers of gravity —procedures that lead to intricate arrangements of tanks, valves, and pumps, fluid-transfer problems, and for some submersibles the irreversible dumping of solid ballast. To date, no robot vehicles have been given such capabilities.

The minimum in guidance equipment for a robot is a horizontal and a vertical reference. It has to know which way is up and at the very least which way it was heading when it was launched. Otherwise no intelligible commands can be issued to it. For direction in the horizontal plane, it must have a gyroscopic device. Vertically, a pendulum is sometimes adequate as a reference. But for a vehicle that is subject to acceleration, vibration, roll, or pitch—and what vehicle isn't?—pendulums have their problems, and generally the more expensive gyroscope is resorted to.

As to payload, it depends on the mission. An oceanographer is interested in packing aboard as many instruments and recording devices as he can. A submarine commander on a war patrol would like to see as many pounds of explosives in his warheads as he can get, plus a reliable and effective homing device, plus a lot of fuel or batteries. On a practice shot, he needs a so-called exercise head, filled with recorders to tell exactly what the torpedo did, when it did it, and where it went; with devices for bringing the torpedo to the surface at the end of the run; and with acoustic pingers and lights to help find it on the surface.

The military torpedo, particularly in its exercise version, is very close to a useful oceanographic tool. One of the first institutions to see the parallel and to make the various system changes required to create a research vehicle was the Applied Physics Laboratory at the University of Washington, which did so in the late 1950s. The laboratory now has several unmanned self-propelled vehicles, as it calls them. They have run repeatedly at depths to 9,000 feet and for a period of up to five hours. Carrying a variety of oceanographic instruments, they have recorded data at the mid-depths that then either were not reachable at all or had been investigated only rarely by older techniques.

Unlike the first space probes, which had no predecessors, the APL instrument has a family tree that through its military ancestry goes back about a century. The reasons that these earlier generations of underwater vehicles were not used in oceanography illustrate some interesting phases in the rapidly accelerating evolution of pure and applied ocean-ography.

A practical, operable, unmanned, self-propelled under-water vehicle has been available since 1868. Because it was self-propelled, a rare characteristic then, it was called by its inventor the automobile torpedo. The inventor was Robert Whitehead, who by the 1870s was among the group of men who had become rich by its manufacture in quantity. If any-one at that time thought of using torpedoes as oceano-graphic instruments, the thought is not well recorded.

Torpedoes were, for one thing, quite expensive, and only governments, under military motivation, felt that they could afford their use. Prior to World War II, when a torpedo, as now, cost considerably more than a Rolls-Royce, the skip-pers of American submarines and destroyers were very re-luctant to fire them in practice. The recovery of a torpedo (or any robot vehicle) at sea remains to this day an uncer-tain matter, and in the economy-minded climate of the 1930s, a ship commander who lost a torpedo was in for a great deal of fuss, much paperwork, and, more than likely, a bad entry in his dossier.

In World War II this policy was to cost us enormous sums of money and more lives than anyone in authority cares to estimate, for it was a year and a half before the major faults in the MK 14, the primary American torpedo of that era, were discovered and eradicated. In the meantime, our sub-marines, the only vessels we then possessed that could enter the great areas of the Pacific commanded by Japanese air and surface power, sank far fewer ships than they could have with adequate weapons, ships that continued to carry Japa-nese soldiers into the Pacific and vital supplies into Japan. But that is all another story.

Aside from the fact that it was almost impossible for an oceanographer to get his hands on a few torpedoes—let alone on the means to keep such specialized and delicate devices in working order—the torpedoes of the past were preset. That is, they ran in a straight line at a fixed depth in one selected direction until they had exhausted their fuel.

A few designers had developed guidance mechanisms that could cause the torpedo to run in selected patterns. These varied from circles to quite elaborate zigzags. The controls, however, were virtually state secrets and hardly to be divulged to some long-bearded oceanographer.

Very little effort was devoted to hulls or to control systems that would permit the torpedo to operate over a wide range of depths, and for two very good reasons. In the first place, torpedoes were intended as weapons to be fired at surface ships. Until the gigantic tankers of the current era came along, surface ships never had drafts that much exceeded thirty-five to forty feet. In the second place, the deeper a torpedo must run, the heavier its hull must be, the more restrictions on the power plant, the more difficult are the problems of sealing against leaks. Sensible torpedo designers of the prewar era did not volunteer to make their torpedoes run deep.

The emergence in World War II of acoustic homing heads opened up, for the first time, the possibility of torpedo attack against submerged submarines. Since then, the most massive torpedo developments of the U.S. Navy, and very likely of other maritime powers, have been concerned with attacking submarines at the greatest depths the latter can reach. The oceanographer has profited substantially by fallout from these programs.

The U.S. Navy has also found several uses for torpedolike

devices other than as weapons. One is to serve as a submarine simulator or as a sonar target. A destroyer intent on practicing its antisubmarine warfare techniques does not find it easy to obtain a submarine to practice with. They are too costly and have too many other missions. There are fewer submarines than destroyers in the U.S. Navy, and the nuclear submarines in particular are loaded down with schedules of tests, training runs, and patrols. Yet there is no natural object in the ocean that acts sufficiently like a submarine to give adequate training to the crew of an antisubmarine vehicle.

Therefore, the Navy has produced some very small mobile devices that can act and sound more or less like submarines. These small robot vehicles can be dropped from a helicopter or launched overboard from a ship at the beginning of an exercise and recovered at the end of it to be recharged and used again. One such simulator is a torpedolike object about thirteen feet long and ten inches in diameter that weighs less than 400 pounds. It can run a series of preset maneuvers for up to three hours at six knots and can put on short bursts of greater speed. It can also change depth, although to a fairly limited degree.

A characteristic of this device that is significant to all undersea robots is that at six knots it needs only a one-fourth-horsepower propulsion motor. Here is a profound difference from space probes, where huge amounts of energy are needed to get them to orbital speed. Small underwater vehicles, manned or unmanned, need trivial amounts of propulsive power as long as they confine themselves to low speeds.

At the moment (hopefully not for long) the oceanographic research probes obtain their energy from electric batteries, the best of which, on an absolute scale, contain relatively little energy for their weight. On war shots, torpedoes use either primary batteries or thermal systems with hydrogen peroxide as the oxidizer. The primary batteries, which use large amounts of silver, are far too expensive for the scientific community; the thermal systems are far too difficult to maintain.

As for their controllability, the mechanical pattern runners of World War II have been overwhelmingly surpassed by a variety—indeed, a dazzling, almost confusing variety—of electronic guidance methods. For most scientific missions it is now quite simple to create control systems that can be commanded during the run to execute new maneuvers on command, to run deeper or shallower, to change course, or even to alter the experiment.

In the ocean the designer has exactly two practical means of communication to choose from: acoustic telemetry or wire. The Germans began development of wire-guided torpedoes during World War II. Since then a large variety of torpedo designs have been so guided. However, the wire must be very fine, and it cannot be dragged through the water. Once it is payed out, it lies dead in the water, and it is not practical to recover it. A strong, heavy cable has such great drag that it can be moved at moderate speed only in shallow water, with robot and ship remaining close together. Basically, a tethered vehicle can go deep only if the support ship is stationary or at very low speed. If it desired to search large horizontal areas fast, the depth separation between control ship and tethered robot is limited.

If this chapter has on occasion looked at automatic and robotlike aids to the oceanographer with less than a complete "isn't science wonderful" point of view, it is not through want of appreciation for their present and future effectiveness. They are valuable aids to search and surveillance over reasonably smooth bottoms. In these and other suitable conditions, they have proved far more effective than divers in preliminary and large-area searches, and far less expensive than manned submersibles.

Small digital computers, small high-performance sonars, and small high-quality navigation systems are already available. They are now very costly, but cost is a problem that time will undoubtedly ameliorate. With such components, a free, mobile vehicle could be given great versatility, the ability to run over rough bottoms safely, and the memory to accept very complex instructions. Were the ocean program funded with the same lavishness as the space program, such devices could be built today.

This is only one of many opportunities for mechanization that will be created in the field of ocean engineering. The role of robots as routine maintenance devices would be brighter than the experience of the past eight or ten years would suggest if only there was more routine maintenance. Most of the apparatus now being planted on the bottom is built not to break down. When it fails, it does so for such a variety of unforeseen reasons that it generally requires a man on the scene to diagnose and to deal with a one-of-a-kind situation. As the number of instrument stations on the ocean floor increase, as the world's population realizes that its weather is largely made in the ocean, as mining and other large-scale industrial uses of the ocean increase, so will opportunities for automatic devices.

The Tools of the Trade

Would a ship with fore and aft cycloidal propellors revolutionize our concepts of maneuverability and hence our operational habits? Can we design an economical 500-ton mothership to launch and retrieve easily a 20-ton submarine in sea state four? Does the catamaran have a promising future as a research ship?
—Some questions from Oceanography 1966, by the National Academy of Sciences, National Research Council

THUS COUCHED in the accents of soap opera this concern over support ships sounds rather hilarious—not quite the sort of question to agitate important members of the establishment. Yet it does, for without support ships very few prolonged at-sea operations can take place. More than half the dollars spent on a program involving deep dives, whether by men or by submarines, is eaten up by the chain of support. The National Research Council estimates that in pure oceanography, every man-month at sea must be matched by five or six man-months on shore. For full effectiveness, a 600-ton oceanographic vessel requires an investment of about $1.5 million in shore facilities.

Headquarters for the *Alvin* operation was for a time over a drugstore in Woods Hole. Although having a few rooms over a drugstore in a town on Cape Cod shows a splendid parsimony on the part of the high command, a small submarine working in the open sea also needs support closer at hand.

Military submarines are built large enough and are sufficiently limited in depth capability so that they can load all the supplies, fuel, spare parts, and equipment that make them independent for the weeks or months of a patrol. When they need repairs they can't handle themselves, they go back to port. Not so a small submersible. It must be towed or carried to its operating area. It is independent only for the few hours of a dive. After that its batteries must be recharged, its equipment checked and repaired, its life support system replenished, and its pilots given a little rest. Before the pilots can lie down in a bunk they have to get out of their cramped submersible. If the submarine has already been hoisted out of the water, there's no problem. If it is bobbing around in the water, it is time to pray for calm weather. In the case of *Aluminaut,* too big to be pulled aboard, getting the crew off in a seaway can be one of the more interesting of the day's operations. Samuel Johnson understood the problem very well: "Being in a ship is being in jail, with the chance of being drowned."

A large support ship is needed even to lift a small submarine clear of the water. Because it rolls easily from off-center forces, a single hull can lift, with the utmost precaution, only a small percentage of its total weight over the side. Heavier weights can be handled over the bow or stern, but these are not always appropriate lifting points. The rougher the sea, the more unpredictable the cable stresses and the more severe the restrictions on weight handling. When the Farrel Lines put a 200-ton crane on one of their 12,000-ton merchant ships some years ago, they established for a while the most powerful lifting device in the American merchant marine. A few Japanese and German freighters, with special pontoons built into their hulls, claimed somewhat larger lift capacities. None of these ships has any intention of exerting their maximum lifts in the open sea.

A submarine cannot be allowed to lie alongside, slammed repeatedly by the irresistible thrust of the waves into the hull of the support ship. Although among the most rugged of vessels, a submarine is, in some respects, more delicate than an egg. An egg can take a blow several times its weight. Not so a submarine, or at least its comparatively fragile superstructure, piping, and other internal components. Nor is it easy to lift a submarine on deck even when a big enough crane is available. The hook needs a "hard point" to grab hold of, and although many small submarines have one or more hard points built in, large stresses on the hull can still occur. Most of the United States government's research submarines have been designed to be transportable by plane and thus tend to weigh less than about thirty tons. There are portents, in *Aluminaut* and in the PX 15, that for the big industrial jobs of the future, much larger work submarines will be needed. With the seventy-ton *Aluminaut* and the more than one hundred-ton PX 15, the current solution is simple. No provision is made to lift them out of the water while at sea.

Ships at sea avoid at all costs touching each other. During refueling operations, tankers and naval vessels remain scores of feet from each other, with only an oil line connecting them. The skippers who have a knack for ship handling under these circumstances become known throughout the fleet. In the Antarctic, when a one hundred-ton killer ship wants to tie up alongside its 40,000-ton factory ship, a dead whale is frequently interposed as a fender. Given the difficul- ties of hoisting any heavy object onto a ship in the open sea, the designer of a support ship who says that he can recover a submarine in waves up to six or seven feet is announcing quite a feat. The official report on the H-bomb search repeatedly refers to the difficulties created by lack of adequate support ships. It draws the obvious conclusion that the weather will always have a massive effect on salvage operations "unless they can be conducted with all task force elements submerged." (The Navy should have other reasons for being interested in a totally submerged support capability, that is, submarine mother ships. Spain cooperated in the hunt for the H-bomb. It is not hard to imagine situations in which a search has to be conducted clandestinely.)

When Woods Hole Oceanographic Institution acquired *Alvin,* it made the happy decision to design its own support ship. Restricted in funds, it ingeniously constructed *Lulu,* a catamaran built out of two surplus Navy pontoons. This lash-up has been so successful that twin-hulled catamarans, now elegantly designed by naval architects, have become rather *de rigueur* as support ships.

A small submarine being recovered by a twin-hulled craft glides in between the hulls, where it finds a partially sheltered patch of water and where the rolling and pitching of the surface ship is least. Whatever the support ship, the operation becomes increasingly hazardous as the sea roughens. The *Alvin* recovery system, is, in Navy parlance, sea state three limited (waves up to about four feet in height). This means that, in New England waters, *Alvin* ceases operation in early fall.

As the Polynesians discovered thousands of years ago, a catamaran is much more stable in rough water than a single hull of equal tonnage. The naval architect measures this difference in terms of the ship's metacentric height, which for a catamaran can be ten or more times that for a displacement hull of equal size. It is implicit that a catamaran should be able to hoist far more weight through its center well than a displacement hull can over the side.

Catamarans are by no means the only kind of hull form with very high stability. Certain forms of semisubmersible oil rigs have even better overall performance characteristics. However, since naval architects are not noted for their enthusiastic advocacy of radical hull forms, perhaps the small submarines should be grateful for the catamaran's rise as a support craft.

The new submarine rescue ships being built as part of the *D*eep *S*ubmergence *R*escue *V*ehicle (DSRV) program are catamarans—big ones. They are 235 feet long and eighty-six feet across (each hull is twenty-six feet wide) and displace over 2,500 tons. The program calls for ten of them to back up six DSRVs. Submarine rescue ships (ASRs) have always been part of the Navy's back-up for its submarine fleet, but without the depth capabilities which the DSRVs will supply.

Assuming that at least some compartments of a damaged submarine are intact, the time the crew can survive depends on a limited air supply. The Navy's aim is to be able by 1970 to place a rescue vehicle on the scene of a disaster anywhere in the world (for that is the area of operations of our submarine fleet) within fifty hours.

In peacetime, many years can lapse between submarine sinkings. Therefore, instead of sitting idly, perhaps for decades, in half a dozen ports strewn around the world, the rescue vessels and their DSRVs will have secondary missions that hopefully will occupy most of their time. The DSRVs, with their 3,500-foot depth capability, can carry out many oceanographic chores. The big catamarans can support divers and a variety of salvage operations.

As soon as the location of a submarine disaster is known, the plan is to transport a DSRV from a base port by truck-trailer to a nearby military cargo plane and fly it to an air-port nearest to the sinking. But wait a minute! Two truck-trailers are necessary, and two large cargo planes. The second set carries the support equipment. Offloaded from the planes, rescue submarine and support gear are trucked to the nearest suitable seaport, that is, one that has the neces-sary large cranes and deep water, and loaded aboard a sup-port ship, if one is available and the weather near the wreck is calm. If the submarine has gone down under the ice or if the seas are rough, the mother ship must be a large sub-marine. (Although a DSRV can be launched and retrieved by a submarine in any weather, a mother submarine made top-heavy by a DSRV on its deck cannot surface in rough water except at great risk.) After arriving at the scene of the sink-ing, the DSRV is released to home on the disabled ship on the bottom—if it can be found. As with the present rescue chambers, the skirt below the DSRV must mate with a smooth ring of metal left clear around all submarine hatches and scarcely four feet in diameter. If the damaged submersi-ble is resting on too steep an incline or has rolled over too far, mating can be impossible. Even with the submarine in an acceptable position, the best pilots in the Navy have encountered difficulty, in simulators, in placing the DSRV in proper condition when turbulent currents are flowing over the wreck.

Whenever an undersea accident occurs, there is the possi-bility that a decompression chamber will be needed. Next to a support ship, this is just about the largest piece of equipment that a diving expedition or a submarine rescue mission needs. A decompression chamber is basically a big cylinder whose interior can be pumped from atmospheric to any pressure that divers or submarine crews might encounter. Some hospitals have similar units, called hyperbaric chambers, in which patients can be placed who are suffering from certain diseases, like gas gangrene, that benefit from an increased oxygen pressure. Such chambers are not particularly complicated. They are just heavy and expensive, and they constitute a sort of ticket of admission to ocean-engineering organizations that intend to support large-scale, deep-diving operations.

Now that a submarine, a support ship, a decompression chamber, and some divers are on hand and have all steamed out to sea, the next standard question to arise is "Where are we, and where is the object on this bottom we are going to inspect, salvage, blow up, mine, or what have you?" When pilots of small submarines shop talk, they are more apt to discuss their latest difficulties in locating their support ship, or their work points on the ocean floor, or a near-collision with some utterly unexpected feature of the bottom than any other single topic. Or they will regale each other with horrendous (and true) stories of errors they found in the bottom contour maps.

In the decade or so since small research submarines of any mobility first started to dive, it has become clear that the problem of location depends very much on where the operation is being conducted. Within sight of land a number of precise and relatively inexpensive techniques are available. Short-range radionavigation systems offer reasonably good fixes (as sailors call a location) to any ship with an antenna above water and the proper receivers on board. This isn't much help to a deeply submerged submarine, but by the use of acoustic beacons placed on the bottom and surveyed in by the surface ships or by various ad hoc subterfuges such as the "fortune cooky" markers used in the *Thresher* search, they get along.

In the open ocean the outlook for underwater navigation to the precision required by many scientific and industrial tasks has been rather bleak until recently. It is not that a ship at sea is overly worried about being so wrong about its location that it fails to find its land fall or runs aground. When the sky is clear, that sort of precision is adequately met by a traditional star fix or a sextant shot at the Sun or Moon. An astronomical fix is good at best to about a mile. In foggy weather, and without the mental gymnastics required of a sextant observation, Loran and Omega will give locations that are generally good to a mile or better. That's great for routine navigation. But if a submarine costs $5,000 a day to operate, its pilot can see a full twenty feet ahead, and he knows he is within a mile of a $1 million treasure, the odds that the venture will show a profit are not excessive.

Or to illustrate with a simpler case, consider Sammy Collins' plight when he first started to mine diamonds off South Africa. By the early 1960s he had acquired leases on over 600 square miles of ocean floor facing a desert and hostile coast. In the relatively shallow water where the diamonds lay the waves were rarely less than twelve feet high and sometimes reached thirty feet. What he was looking for were stones that almost never exceeded half an inch in their maximum dimension.

Diamonds are not found scattered thickly on a quiet and sandy ocean floor, as they were on the bottom of Sinbad's valley. Of the millions of tons of water, sand, and gravel that are pumped aboard the mining dredges, only a few parts per million are diamonds. And these are found, even in such small concentrations, only in certain cracks and channels that have trapped them over the ages. No profit is to be had in mining areas where expensive photographic and sonic surveys have indicated very few if any diamonds exist or in redredging an area over which tailings (the waste material of the mining process) had previously been pumped overboard. Thus the mining dredges must at all times know exactly where they are. This they were able to do in the African venture and at a reasonable cost by drawing on long-existing optical surveying techniques (for they are generally in sight of land) and by using precise radionavigation techniques. Primarily because of optical ranging on shore beacons, the dredges generally can be positioned within about three feet.

At the opposite extreme is the dilemma of a submarine that must run a precisely located course in the open ocean. Now that the U.S. Navy has released for general use the *Transit* satellite and the associated ship-carried electronics (a major development in navigation that has been compared in importance to the introduction of the chronometer), a surface ship can locate itself in latitude and longitude to an accuracy of at least a tenth of a mile, and perhaps to within 300 feet. The submarine can start its dive to within that accuracy. If it were to dead-reckon its course thereafter by conventional means (gyrocompass and speed log), it would soon be badly in error due to currents and instrument errors. If someone had surveyed the bottom and had located landmarks or had placed beacons with great precision, that would solve the pilot's problem. But such an assumption partly begs the question. Very little of the ocean floor has been accurately surveyed. If some peculiar and unmistakable contour is found but its position is incorrectly reported, the resultant map is no great help. In the seventeenth and eighteenth centuries, navigators frequently reported new islands, which would then be lost for generations. Succeeding mariners cruising to the alleged latitude and longitude would find nothing but open water. They were marching, so to speak, to the light vibrations of another star.

One of the better methods of precise underwater navigation for a submarine, particularly when coupled to a good fixed reference like an acoustic marker, is an inertial system. It has been known for decades that an assembly of three gyroscopes and three accelerometers could, in principle, be made to stand fixed in space, free of Earth's rotation. If the platform were pointed at one of the fixed stars, there it can point indefinitely. Or conversely, as one moved such a platform over Earth, it could tell precisely how far it had moved—that is, if the gyroscopes were perfectly balanced and the accelerometers without error.

World War II, with its enormous appetite for gyroscopic instruments, accelerated the march to perfection of the necessary components. A landmark was reached when the Polaris program, which required that a submarine know its exact location on the Earth after days of submergence, forced the development of SINS (Submarine Inertial Navigation System). The first units were big and needed a digital computer of rather impressive capability to help run them, as they still do. But intensive engineering resulted in progressively smaller and more accurate systems. Today, inertial navigation systems less than a foot in diameter and digital computers microminiaturized so that they can sit on the palm of a man's hand are available. Thus, the underwater navigation problem of the submerged submarine is solved—well, not quite. As of 1968 few research or work submarines used such a platform. They couldn't afford to. That problem time will solve.

Speaking of submarine rescue ships, and of submarine support ships generally, one of their imperfectly solved problems is how to communicate with their charges below. In the case of the *Thresher,* the first indication that something was wrong was a garbled and incomplete call via the underwater telephone. Messages via the acoustic telephone are subject to so many interruptions even in so-called normal conditions that it is not hard to understand the rescue ship's bewilderment and delay before calling for help.

Skippers of submarines being what they are, the manager of a diving operation who likes to stay on top of his job can anticipate more than technical problems in his communications system. Let us say that our gung-ho project manager cranks up his underwater telephone and finds that it is working admirably. He asks, "How are things down below?" Answer: "O.K." "But what is your CO_2 reading?" Answer, complete with echos, "Look, Mac, we're busy. Don't call us again. We'll call you."

One way out is to relieve the busy pilots of routine reports on the status of their vehicle. This sort of reporting can be done better by automatic telemetry. Such automatic monitoring systems, in principle like those that tie space vehicles to the ground control stations are, with qualifications, within the state of the art. They cannot have the data capacity of the space links because the latter are based on high-frequency radio carriers that can handle millions of bits of data per second. If the data must be sent acoustically through thousands of yards of water, far less data can be transmitted. An offsetting factor is that manned submarines are in a safer position than a space craft. If anything goes wrong, but not catastrophically so, they can simply abort the mission and rise to the surface.

The diver's problem in communicating to his support crew on the surface or to his buddies is tougher than that of a small submarine in part because he can't carry as much equipment or expend as much electrical power. And he is up against some built-in physiological barriers.

With two good ears, a human being who is operating in the atmosphere into which he was born can tell rather accurately from which direction a sound is coming. To tell whether a footfall in the night is to one side or to the rear, to look in the right direction at the occurrence of a sudden sound, has considerable survival value. The ears have other localizing capabilities. They can separate the first arrival of a sound from its echoes—the so-called precedence effect. In a factory or in a crowded room, they can pick out and concentrate on one source of noise or on one conversation out of many—derisively but accurately called the cocktail party effect.

All of this is possible because the delay between the time the same sound reaches one ear and then the other can be close to 1/1000 second. Furthermore, the human head, in air, is rather impervious to sound waves. It acts like a baffle, letting each ear have its own access to the sound source.

Put this same man in water, in which sound travels almost five times faster than in air, and he is completely confused. Since his head is composed mainly of material that is not much denser than water, sound goes through it almost as if it were transparent. The time differences to which his ears and brain neutrons have become accustomed through millennia of evolution and a lifetime of training become vanishingly small. He can no longer tell from which direction a sound is coming. Reverberations boom in so fast that he loses the precedence effect that in air helps him locate a sound source. Echoes override and smear a conversation. When he talks over one of the many kinds of underwater telephones that have been developed, he must overcome the noise of his exhaled air bubbling into the water. Increasing the density of the gases in a man's mouth, larynx, and lungs will affect his speech regardless of the composition of the gases. Using helium as the inert constituent of the mixture just makes a bad situation worse. If, in addition, he has a breathing tube clenched between his teeth, he has a worse problem of enunciation than did Demosthenes with his pebbles. Once his mutterings get into the microphone and are broadcast on an acoustic carrier, something can be made out by the listener as long as the range is short. As distance increases, all present underwater telephones, to a greater or lesser extent, run into trouble with noise pick-up, fading, reverberations, and echoes that can repeat in phenomenal number. Today many divers use a slate on which to record their observations, and pressurized tape recorders are available for the affluent.

Divers can have problems with seeing as well as with hearing. "Good visibility" is frequently defined by divers as any condition that lets them see more than three feet. When visibility is not good, the diver must feel his way or he must resort to sonar. In an absolute sense, the hand-held sonars now available are quite remarkable. An experienced operator can learn to understand from the echo quite a bit about the nature of the area around him. For example, he can tell a pile of rocks by a mushy echo or he can tell that the ping is coming from a small, hollow float by a sharp echo. Under ideal conditions these small, high-frequency sonars can pick up objects the size of beer cans. "Ideal" means something like a flat, sand bottom. To keep the capability of these devices in perspective, however, it should be remembered that sonar has been frequently attempted as a guide to the blind, not yet with anything approaching complete success.

By and large, divers do not attempt any delicate operations in black water and they do not use delicate tools. An explosive-powered stud driver or an oxyacetylene cutting torch is a more typical diver aid. Both commercial and military divers frequently want to plant some heavy piece of apparatus in a precise position on the bottom or want to lift an even heavier wreck off the bottom and get it to the surface. Because there are apt to be objections if the skipper casually pushes an instrument package (worth perhaps, several Rolls Royces) off the deck, some gentler technique must be sought. If it is lowered from a winch, the package is not likely to reach the bottom in exactly the spot or the orientation desired. Inevitably, a diver has to handle the package himself, and in these circumstances he must have the equivalent of a hoist or a fork-lift truck.

This generally takes the form today of a floatation balloon. At any particular depth the diver can just about balance out the weight of the object he is handling by pumping air into the floatation bag. However, if the bag gets away from him and starts to rise, it will rise faster and faster as the gas inside the bag expands and creates more buoyancy. For this reason a controllable bleed-off valve on the top of the floatation bladder is necessary. Such underwater diver-control floatation devices have been used for several years for lifting objects weighing up to almost a ton in water. A still simpler device is to use a parachute. The divers trap their exhaust air under it until it begins to lift. This method is less controllable than the floatation bag. Left to itself the parachute will rise faster and faster as it approaches the surface.

Controlling these lifting devices is not made easier by the fact that an object, like an old wreck that has become imbedded in the mud, needs a "breakout" force that is generally far greater than the force required to lift it. When they can, divers resort to jets of water to loosen or remove the soil around a wreck, or they dig a tunnel under the wreck through which they can pass a sling. Frequently there is nothing on the object they are trying to salvage to which they can attach a rope. Ships do not normally come equipped with hard points and lifting pads. Thus, the diver needs to know enough about the structure he is salvaging so that when he does attach a lifting pad with his stud driver it will not be to some flimsy piece of plating or that his drill will not penetrate into a pocket of compressed gas.

Since hoists mounted on ships can rarely provide enough lift to bring up a ship, pontoons or chemical foams are used to provide floatation. Rigid steel pontoons are clumsy to handle and must be ballasted to sink.

Collapsible rubber pontoons are generally easier to handle, as are chemicals that can be injected into a hull, and then foam into a rigid, buoyant material. A variant of the plastic-foam concept, used to raise a Danish merchant ship that sank in 114 feet of water in a Greenland port, was to blow small, hollow plastic balls into the hull. Although relatively expensive, the technique was resorted to in an effort to save diver man-hours. The vessel went down in water that was close to freezing and in which the divers could work for very short periods. After first strengthening the decks and hatches of the ship so that they could withstand the lifting load, the divers burned a hole into the side of the ship and blew in the bubbles until the hull floated. It took nine divers from mid-May to early July to raise this 3,000-ton ship.

In the sense that a dog or a horse is a tool to man, so may become the porpoise. One of the most exciting and unexpected results of the many years of work that have now gone into experiments with porpoises is a possibility that these animals may become assistants to divers in perhaps a fuller sense that a dog is an assistant to a shepherd. Because the porpoise is such an efficient submersible, and has such extraordinary sonar, the Navy has for many years been funding a variety of investigations of its physiology and behavior. By and large an animal's sensing equipment is so much more complex and so utterly different from anything an engineer can build that very few, if any, useful connections have so far been made. However, in the course of this work it has been found that porpoises, among the most intelligent of mammals, can be trained to a variety of complicated tasks, and that when let loose in the ocean they will not attempt to escape, but will come back to their trainers. Investigators, wishing to learn how fast a porpoise could swim when unimpeded by the walls of a tank (for porpoises, like jet planes, are so streamlined they have trouble slowing down), released a Hawaiian bottlenosed porpoise in an open bay off Oahu. "The little porpoise was reluctant to leave the friendly and familiar confines of his lagoon. Once outside," continued Kenneth S. Norris, "he chattered his jaws in fright and raced away, seeking the safety of the lagoon entrance. Missing that, he plunged along the coral-fringed shore toward the open bay beyond." The recall signal was sounded, and the porpoise, "now 1000 yards away, whirled and raced back to the open boat."

Further work has demonstrated that observations of wild porpoise schools in the open sea, although as difficult a chore in animal observation as can be imagined, is possible and of great potential. Wild porpoises may swim thirty to fifty miles a day. Unlike their tame brethren confined to shallow tanks, they fully use the ocean's third dimension. When they dive they head practically straight down and quickly disappear from view. To help observe these porpoises underwater Norris has devised some towed floats that permit an observer to sit about six feet below the surface. The first such float, devised from a surplus auxiliary fuel tank for a jet plane, became known as "Norris' Nausea Machine."*

Porpoises have a phenomenal ability to find and recognize the nature of small objects in the water. They can tell the difference between one species of fish and another of equal size, or between a dead fish and a live fish. In one experiment on the west coast the Navy has trained porpoises to locate torpedoes on the bottom. Of course, porpoises do not have hands like people and cannot attach wires and so on to an object on the bottom, but they can drop a specially prepared marker near the object that has one end weighted to stay on the bottom while the other end floats to the top. Porpoises have also shown that they can be taught to find divers lost on the bottom and help to rescue them. If the diver is saturated, and cannot return to the surface, the porpoise must guide him to an underwater habitat. The first porpoises to be trained in this procedure were the Atlantic

* Kenneth S. Norris, "Studying Porpoises in their Natural Habitat," *Naval Research Reviews*, August 1968, Vol. XXI, No. 8, p. 1.

bottlenose porpoises, who generally live in shallow water. Divers can already operate at depths beyond the natural capabilities of these animals, and some varieties of deep-water Pacific dolphins are being trained to work with the divers in *SeaLab III*.

Platforms and Habitats

Henceforth the current will be our motive power, while our ship, no longer a means of transport, will become a barrack, and we shall have ample time for scientific observations.

—Dr. Fridtjof Hansen, *from the address of 1890 in which he described his plan, carried out a few years later, to build the Fram, deliberately sail her into the ice, and from this platform, now frozen into immobility, demonstrate for the first time the major currents, the great depths, the absence of land under the Pole, and other oceanographic characteristics of the Arctic Ocean*

ONE OF THE DUTIES of the U.S. Coast Guard is to properly mark dangers to navigation. As part of that responsibility the Coast Guard prepares charts to show where the safe channels lie and how to recognize obstructions. Occasionally an old obstruction is removed or a new menace to navigation entered on the map, but it has not, in the past, been a field marked by frenzied activity.

Off Louisiana and Texas, however, some 7,000 "artificial islands" were, in 1967, concrete evidence of the billions of dollars that the oil industry is pouring every year into offshore exploration. Most of these "islands" are fixed platforms sitting on the bottom on long columns of steel. In deeper water, they are more apt to be mobile rigs—barges, "jack-up," and semisubmergible structures, even full-fledged ships. The situation is not unique. "Lake" Maracaibo, in Venezuela, an almost-closed-off bay of the sea, now contains over 5,000 platforms. From the air this area, smaller than several of our Great Lakes, looks like a surrealistic forest, sprouting iron trees in geometric arrays. Eventually such forests will fringe all the continents and most of the earth's larger islands. Oil companies are currently drilling off the shores of some seventy countries. There are less than one hundred nations with maritime borders of significant length.

Most of these structures now hug the world's continental rims, where the water is shallow. But thousands of the world's offshore wells are producing oil in deeper water, as far as seventy miles from land and as deep as 340 feet. That is, today. By 1970 many wells may be as much as 150 or more miles from shore. Exploration wells have already been drilled in waters beyond the continental shelves. Economics aside, it is now technically possible to drill in water of virtually any depth. As wells go deeper, more and more of the control equipment will be mounted and maintained on the bottom. How many wells will there eventually be in the sea? Over two million have been drilled on land.

In United States waters, the Coast Guard requires that submerged structures extending to within eighty-five feet of the surface be marked by a lighted buoy to warn navigators. What concerns the Coast Guard is that these new navigation aids already number 14,000 in the Gulf of Mexico and are growing at about 1,000 per year.

To be useful these navigation aids must be surveyed so that their position is accurately known and properly marked on charts. The hazards that cartographers have traditionally dealt with have been geological features that, except in the rarest instances, stayed put. Occasionally a new wreck, a new dumping ground for explosives, or a new light might require marking, but rarely did sudden or drastic changes to shipping channels occur. If the increase in offshore obstructions is left unchecked, ship routes will be forced farther and farther to sea—thus, the need to clear or maintain "fairway," or safe channels for ocean traffic. This problem has arisen, or soon will, in many of the world's seas.

The erection of so many offshore structures that they become a traffic hazard is important if one is a shipmaster. Otherwise this aspect of ocean engineering is an oblique and partial light on the growing amount of construction that is taking place in the sea. In addition to the thousands of platforms erected by the oil industry and a very few put up by miners of solid minerals are the platforms positioned by governments to serve as navigation markers, as radar posts, and as oceanographic observatories.

Italy, a relatively small and densely populated country, has created an application for a floating platform that may give her small space program more flexibility in choosing launch sites that even a large country possesses. She has mounted a rocket launching pad on one platform and a radar and optical tracking station on another. Thus the noisy and potentially dangerous business of a rocket launch can be performed in areas that are not only far from populated centers but also have the latitude or longitude best suited to a particular experiment. This is an obvious advantage in tracking a solar eclipse; or, if an equatorial orbit is desired, the rocket can get a not inconsequential boost from the earth's peripheral velocity, if the platforms are towed to some spot near the Equator.

Floating platforms are being contemplated that are big

enough to take a jet runway. These are not artificial islands, which are more a tribute to the efficiency of modern earth-moving equipment than to ocean technology. Real estate on or surrounded by water has always had a high relative value, and in densely populated areas, the scarcity of open sites near water is now chronic. To solve these space problems by the dredge, as is being done with increasing frequency throughout the world, often creates difficult problems in the conservation of biological resources and does not always remove sufficiently the nuisance of planes, which continue to become faster, heavier, and noisier. Deeper areas of the sea, farther from shore, are being eyed as the place to put these planes down. In Japan, the United States, and Europe, floating airports are under active investigation.

One of the best-known oceanographic platforms is stationed about thirty miles southwest of Bermuda on the top of an ancient sea mount. This is the Argus Island, which, among its other duties, served as a support station for *Sea-Lab I*. The Mine Defense Laboratory, Florida, operates two in the Gulf of Mexico, and the Naval Electronics Laboratory has built one off San Diego.

Although these platforms tend to be lonely posts, there are worse laboratories for oceanographers. To remain in the atmosphere, surrounded by masses of instrumentation, in contact with deep water, yet not on a rolling, pitching, yawing ship is next door to paradise for an oceanographer, whose basic occupational hazard is seasickness.

Fixed platforms begin to encounter serious difficulties as the water deepens below 200 feet. Hardly half a dozen platforms had been installed in more than 300 feet of water as this section was written. An oil-well rig that can jack itself up to 300 feet or so above the bottom runs about $7 million and up at the shipyard, before it is towed to its station and properly sunk into place. All these platforms must be able to face winds and waves of hurricane proportions. If they must also withstand the 15-million-pound pressure of ice floes being pushed by 6-knot currents, as they do in Alaska's Cook Inlet, this price goes up to $12 million and more.

To work in water deeper than 300 feet today requires a floating rig. (The term "platform" is generally restricted to a structure that rests more or less permanently on legs.) There is nothing absolute in this limit. It is a matter of economics and technology. In a few years the division between fixed and floating platforms may be at some other depth.

Floating rigs come in a bewildering variety of forms. The evolutionary process that will eventually demonstrate the best designs has not yet had enough time to operate in this rapidly expanding field. Many are converted from standard ship hulls of several thousand tons' displacement by mounting a large enough derrick amidship and by constructing a well in the center of the ship so that the drill pipes can be dropped down to the bottom. An increasing number are catamarans, expensive but of great stability. The majority are called semisubmersibles—floating rigs that are designed around a series of buoyancy chambers.

In all these floating rigs the least visible but perhaps most important feature is the system of sensors, controls, and cables and anchors (or with increasing frequency, the controllable propellers) that keep the platform over a given point on the ocean floor regardless of winds, waves, and currents. In really deep water, no system of anchors can hold the ship accurately enough and only the controllable propellers will do. In effect, such drill ships are anchored by computers. The accuracy with which these systems can hold a chosen position can be better than 1 percent of depth. In other words, in water 4,000 feet deep, the platform will move laterally less than forty feet from a chosen position (the drill hole) until winds and waves become overpowering.

A floating rig held in place by propellers—that is, dynamically—makes it possible to drill in any depth of water. For scientific purposes cores have been drilled in water approaching two miles in depth. However, even if the geology of the deep sea floors proves conducive to oil deposits and even if the drills locate oil, it probably could not be economically recovered from such depths today.

Although dwarfed by the semisubmersible rigs, which can weigh up to 15,000 tons, the catamarans used for drilling at sea are twin-hulled ships hundreds of feet long and thousands of tons in displacement.

Because of the high and heavy derricks and the deckloads of pipes and casings, drill ships can encounter heavy overturning torques when winds or seas are high. And in almost every area in which offshore wells must be drilled, if one goes back far enough in time, the records seem invariably to confirm that winds exceeding one hundred miles an hour will occasionally be encountered.

Unlike a ship, which makes money only when it is moving as rapidly as possible from one port to another, a floating drill rig earns its keep only when it is hovering with no more than a few yards of motion over a fixed point on the bottom. If it has to be towed once or twice a year, or even every month, from one site to another, not much is lost. The semisubmersible rig therefore need bear no resemblance to a ship. Generally it is a collection of huge cylindrical buoyancy chambers arranged vertically on the perimeter of a triangular or rectangular plan. These chambers are connected by steel beams on which, here and there as needed, is a platform. Otherwise one can look thirty or fifty feet down to water. These semisubmersible rigs are quite "transparent" to waves. To a naval architect, the term "transparent" means that the "hull," if a collection of big vertical pipes can be called a hull, tends to ignore wave forces. Up to 300 feet wide in every direction, and with their main buoyancy well below the zone of wave action, these rigs are exceptionally indifferent to wave-induced motion. They are also big and expensive, renting at rates that can exceed $10 per minute. They must be big. By the time a well is deep and a long string of pipe is hanging on the hook, the platform must handle loads running into the millions of pounds. When their derricks start to lift the drill pipe, the semisubmersible rigs show a characteristic that can be disconcerting to the uninitiated. Instead of the load coming up, the platform first sinks down. The reason of course is that most of the buoyancy of these platforms is deliberately placed far below the waterline. The columns that intersect the water surface are relatively thin. It can take several feet of descent to create the added displacement to balance a million-pound load.

The most radical concept in platform design—one not yet given a full-scale test—is to use an air-cushion vehicle. The deck of an air-cushion platform is intrinsically well isolated from wave-induced motion. These soft-hulled craft may be more economical to build than orthodox semisubmersibles. A prototype platform fifty feet in diameter has been built, but platforms many hundreds of feet in diameter are feasible.

The "transparent" semisubmersibles are not the only

structures being built to take advantage of the principle, known for many years, that if a floating platform is to remain nearly motionless in a constantly moving sea, most of the buoyancy must be placed below the zone of wave motion.

A number of giant spar buoys, as long and almost as big as an ocean-going ship, have been built that apply this principle full force. When these buoys are floating horizontally, one end has a vaguely bow-shaped appearance, to permit easy towing. The other end, whatever it may be called, contains tanks that can be flooded, so the entire structure "flips" (actually it is done very slowly) to a vertical position, with the heavy end as much as 300 feet below the ocean surface. A long ladderway, running along the centerline of the hull, permits the observers to select the depths at which they wish to work, in air and at atmospheric pressure. Not all these spar buoys, however, are manned; some are equipped only with automatic recording equipment.

The first of these big spar buoys, called FLIP (Floating Instrument Platform)—355 feet overall and 600 tons displacement—was launched in 1962. It was without a doubt the largest spar buoy every built up to that time. In its first five years of operations it has "flipped" 115 times. As it has proved its usefulness to a variety of oceanographic missions, it has grown in weight by some forty tons, by addition of radars, navigation equipment, winches, and more living space for crew. It can now accommodate fourteen persons. Because it is operated by the Scripps Institution of Oceanography in California, most of its operations have been in the Pacific.

In waves of four to five feet, FLIP moves up and down about two inches. In severe storms that would send most of the passengers of a cruise ship to their cabins, FLIP bobs up and down less than a foot and rolls hardly at all. Entering one of the ship-size compartments in such a buoy can momentarily jolt one's sense of orientation, for all the equipment, even the diesel engines, are mounted in bearings so that they will operate "right side up" whether the hull is vertical or horizontal.

Cousteau has also built a gigantic spar buoy (rather like an amphora in shape) with seven working levels extending down 150 feet below the surface.

These various platforms, floating or fixed, do not have the prerogative of a ship in a storm, to seek a haven or to run in a direction that will minimize the punishment they take from the waves. The fixed platforms in particular must stand exposed to wave action for years, running the risk that the constant buffeting, the steady corrosion, or some cataclysmic event like a hurricane will send them toppling. Platforms have been so completely swept away that even the stumps of the heavy steel legs, many feet in diameter, were far below the surface. Only recently has it become at all routine to send divers down with ultrasonic testers and other instrumentation to check on the welds and on the general soundness of the structure. Some platforms have gone down with scores of casualties. Insurance rates have run as high as 10 percent of the risk per year, creating premiums in the hundreds of thousands of dollars per platform.

Since 1961, when the Coast Guard replaced its lightship *Buzzards Bay* with an eighty-foot tower, at least half a dozen positions formerly so marked—among them Breton Reef, off Narragansett Bay; Frying Pan, off Cape Fear; and in 1966 Diamond Shoals, off Cape Hatteras—have acquired towers. It is a bargain for the Coast Guard. Lightships, in the order of 1,000 tons' displacement, needed a crew of about sixteen men and have to be supplied by ship. The steel-legged platforms, riding eighty to ninety feet above the water, take a crew of six and can be supplied at less cost and far more convenience by helicopter.

Then the program came temporarily to a halt, for the towers that had apparently made obsolete the lightships in all but deep water (such as is found off our Pacific coast) appear in turn in danger of obsolescence. Because of the great amount of attention that has been focused on deep-water moors, it is becoming increasingly feasible to anchor large buoys, whatever the storm conditions and depth. Several fully automated buoys, some of them displacing up to fifty tons, have been built. Completely unmanned, capable of being remotely commanded by radio, they give indications that they can remain safely moored and properly operational under conditions of extreme violence. Thus, the Coast Guard's replacement program waits, as of this writing, until it is determined whether these unattended buoys can become a successful substitute for the lightship.

Another application that should use thousands of buoys, if they can be safely moored in deep water, is the marking of shipping lanes hundreds of miles long to keep traffic approaching major ports in controlled areas and thus, hopefully, cut down on collisions. Still another application that could use hundreds of buoys is a world weather watch (WWW), which the world's major maritime nations are slowly implementing. The world's weather maps that are now being drawn several times a day and have incalculable economic significance will thus indeed come from the entire world; rather than from the 30 percent of the earth's surface covered by land.

Particularly for the buoys and smaller floating rigs, the weight, cost, and engineering difficulties of the mooring—as the structure of floats, swivels, cables, and anchors is called— represent a large fraction of the total cost. Only in the last decade have deep-water moors been attempted with a fair degree of success. In the late 1940s, a mooring in 600 fathoms (3,600 feet) was considered extreme. Since then, as stainless-steel fittings and a variety of cables spun from nylon, dacron, and polypropylene (which is buoyant in sea water) have become widely available, taut- and slack-line moors have become reasonably practical in deep water—at least the oceanographer no longer expresses surprise when he finds his buoy in place after a stormy winter.

One of the indications that the oil companies are in earnest about drilling in deeper water is the permits that the Department of the Interior granted to four major American oil companies in 1967 to begin exploration of the conti- nental slope, the area of the ocean bottom that drops down from the 100-fathom (600 feet) curve. "We are not drilling for oil," said the oil companies' spokesman, "but are simply accumulating basic data for further study."

Yet oil is comparatively easy to bring to the surface and to transport to a harbor, as compared with solid minerals. The standard mining devices for shallow water—bucket lad- der dredges and surface pump hydraulic dredges—become dis- couragingly expensive as depths drop off below about 150 feet. However, the air lift dredge may be effective to far greater depths.

The various scientific panels that have considered mining the ocean bottom have almost unanimously predicted that the ocean floor, at least in continental-shelf areas, will even- tually contain large, manned installations. Today, however, only the drills can get far into the bottom in deep water. In 1961 a 600-foot hole was drilled in water that was almost two miles deep. This was one of the series of test bores to prove the feasibility of the Mohole project. Since then, scientific curiosity has resulted in a number of very deep test bores, some at depths measured in miles. For a while, the United States government mounted an attempt to drill to the Mohorovičič discontinuity, but this project was so beset by political and technical disputes and ran up so vast a budget that it has been shelved, at least temporarily.

Andrija Mohorovičič was a Yugoslav who, on the basis of his observations on a 1909 earthquake in Croatia, postulated that underlying the rocklike crust of the earth was a layer of dense elastic material whose characteristics continue to puzzle the geologists. Because the earth's crust, although composed of heavier materials, is believed to be much thinner under the deep ocean basins than on land, the shortest path to the Mohorovičič discontinuity appears to be through the ocean floor. It is believed that this discontinuity may be 20,000 feet or less below some parts of the ocean floor. (There have been hints that, by the use of tremendous derricks and improved drilling equipment, it may be easier to drill to it on land, even if the actual hole has to penetrate twice as far, perhaps to 40,000 feet.)

Mohorovičič came to his conclusions by the same technique used today to locate oil deposits. The earthquake, as does an explosion, sent pressure waves speeding through the various layers that make the earth look in cross section like a very complicated onion. The speed of sound in a material is a function of its density, temperature, and other properties. Thus, the number of different layers the sound passes through and something about their composition can be deduced from the differing times of arrival of a sound wave whose origin is known.

The oil companies expend thousands of pounds of explosives every month "shooting" areas at sea in their search for formations that may contain oil. The seismic records so obtained are guarded like state secrets. Frequently, each company interested in a parcel that a government may later put up for bids will do its own prospecting, to the repeated consternation of the local fishes. Yet frequently several companies will group together to get one joint record of the area, depending in part on the economic arrangements they have in mind.

The reason for explosives is that until recently, no sonars were available that would generate sufficient energy to penetrate tens of thousands of feet into the rock layers below the bottom. Mohorovičič, after all, used an earthquake as his sound source. Today, however, a number of special acoustic devices are available that can generate pulses of energy powerful enough to give some picture of the underlying strata. Although drilling at sea tends to be more expensive than drilling on land, the oil companies have found that their marine exploration costs are sharply lower.

The expanding variety and functions of the fixed and floating platforms and the immense investment being made in them must not obscure the fact that billions of dollars are invested in equipment entirely on the ocean floor—in the thousands of miles of pipelines and in hundreds of thousands of miles of telephone and telegraph cables. Their significance is known fully only to the select group of men in government and industry whose power and responsibility require routine use of the world's transoceanic communications. Since the first underwater cable was laid in 1950 by the steam tug *Goliath,* over 400 ships have been used as cable layers.

In spite of the rise of communication satellites and their ability to transmit some forms of communication trans-oceanically more economically than cables, the world continues to lay underwater cable. Most of these new cables contain high-capacity telephone lines for use between continents or between the continents and nearby islands. Trans-oceanic calls are increasing more rapidly than all but a very few sections of the telephone industry. An American with an itch for long-distance telephoning can now speak directly to Greenland, Qatar, or indeed about 90 percent of the world's telephones. Between 1965 and 1967, trans-Atlantic calls were increasing at the rate of about 20 percent per year, ten times faster than the population.

The varied capabilities of satellites—for communication, for exploration, for geological and oceanographic studies, for gathering weather data, and for military surveillance—are in themselves an insurance that a place will remain for underwater cables. The satellites show signs of becoming a victim of their spectacular success by indulging in a "population explosion." Estimates have been made that close to 300 satellites will be orbiting this globe by the 1980s. Each will exert a claim on some part of the radio spectrum. No matter what their geographic separation (and some orbits are far more desirable than others), such competition should eventually make it attractive to connect more areas of high-density traffic by cables, which cause no external interference.

The deep seas are an ideal area for certain forms of scientific and military surveillance. Geologists are pleased by the absence of man-made disturbances and like to place seismographs on the abyssal plains. Oceanographic institutes frequently place instrument packages in deep water to study bottom currents and temperatures, to learn more about the peculiar chemistry of the great depths, and for many other reasons. The easiest way to get electric power to these packages and to learn what they are recording is to run a cable to them, at approximately $10,000 per mile or, in the rounder numbers that are more appropriate to oceanic distances, at $1 million per hundred miles. The multichannel telephone cables that can carry many hundreds of calls simultaneously are far more expensive.

In a few cases, very high-capacity cables are used to connect the electric grids of geographically separate land masses, such as those of England and France—or, on a smaller scale, those of Connecticut and Long Island. For these various reasons, hardly any major maritime power is without a fleet of cable-laying ships, privately or nationally owned.

Large amounts of cables and instrumentation are now being concentrated in underwater ranges. The first of these underwater ranges, which are worth some comment in their own right, was installed by the Applied Physics Laboratory, Washington State University, in Dabob Bay about a decade ago. Dabob Bay, an arm of Puget Sound, is the deepest body of confined water within the territorial limits of the continental United States. The range is big enough and deep enough (600 feet) to permit a ship or submarine to run in an essentially normal manner. Precisely positioned acoustic arrays coupled by cables to computers on shore measure the performance of military ships and of their complex equipment with an hitherto unavailable accuracy. One of the most startling of this range's early findings was the size of the errors that frequently and unsuspectedly existed in standard equipment on shipboard.

The early instrumented ranges have proved so valuable as

measuring and aligning devices that several much larger ranges have been built. Most of them, like the ones off St. Croix and Hawaii, are in open water. The Autec range in the Bahamas, however, is mounted in the 4,000–6,000 feet-deep recesses of the Tongue of the Ocean. This huge, steep-sided valley, shaped like a cow's tongue, bites for over one hundred miles into the Great Bahama Bank, over most of which the water is less than twenty feet deep. Lying just to the east of Andros Island, it is roughly 150 miles from Miami. The several instrumented ranges that have been installed at a cost of over $130 million (and worth every penny if this country wants fighting ships that not only look impressive but also can shoot impressively) occupy only a fraction of the valley's area. They will test the accuracy and behavior of the Navy's underwater sensors like sonars and sonobuoys and the behavior of its underwater weapons. When a torpedo disappeared underwater in the past, all that could be learned of its performance had to be deciphered from recorders carried in the torpedo's head. If the torpedo was recovered, if the recording equipment worked, if someone had remembered to put film in the oscillograph, if no water had leaked in, some of the events that had transpired inside the weapon were known. But as homing weapons have become standard equipment and as their interaction with targets and decoys has become more intricate, the total situation had to be observed from the outside, by accurate and reliable equipment. Real ships are big; they need thousands of yards just to make a high-speed turn. Today's torpedoes can run for many miles and can descend to great depths. It takes a big, deep range to permit a realistic evaluation of their capabilities.

The main equipment for the underwater ranges are scores of acoustic hydrophones accurately positioned on the bottom. On shore are the radars, optical trackers, meteorological equipment, computers, and the other paraphernalia of a tracking station. The total system, not yet complete, is tied together by over 600 miles of underwater cable. An unique facility is a series of deep-water moors that can hold ships stationary in water over a mile deep.

Like all man's works, this underwater equipment occasionally goes out of order. At these depths, one does not send for a technician with a screwdriver, or even a diver. Nor is it palatable to just scrap the offending equipment and replace it with new. *Autec I,* a submarine of roughly the same size and capability as *Alvin,* has been built to help solve some of the inevitable inspection and maintainence problems.

A basically similar problem is arising as underwater pipelines keep increasing in number and length. They are expensive, running at about $250,000 and up per mile, and thousands of miles have already been installed. To date, most of the pipe laying has been in the Gulf of Mexico; underwater pipelines have also been built in the Persian Gulf, the North Sea, and many other areas. One can hardly build a one hundred-mile pipeline in one piece on shore and float it out to sea, or at least this technique has not been tried. Generally, a specially equipped barge welds the pipe in sections and drops it over the stern. Customarily, a diver walks the pipe as it is payed out, reporting any trouble as it develops. This job is no sinecure under any conditions. As pipelines are put into colder and deeper waters, their inspection will eventually require a cross between Superman and a shark. Without doubt, submarines will eventually replace the divers, so that the inspection can be carried out in shirt-sleeve comfort and the inspection crew can run an eight-hour shift rather than coming up exhausted every hour or so.

The underwater or quasi-underwater structures that have so far been mentioned are highly engineered devices—stationary platforms, mobile rigs, cables, instrument packages, and the like. Another valuable and increasingly frequent structure on the bottom is an artificial reef. It was noted decades ago that whenever a ship went down in coastal waters it soon created a favorable environment for a variety of ocean plants, invertebrates, and fish. What before had been an almost-deserted sandy bottom became a haven for underwater life. Like other animals, most fish require shelter and a fixed supply of food. On a featureless bottom there are few places of anchorage for the many plants, mollusks, and other invertebrates that form the foundation of the ocean community of life. And there are no crannies or nooks in which fish can find shelter. A coral reef offers this opportunity, but inevitably, because of its need for sunlight, rises too close to the surface and becomes a menace to navigation. Man-made reefs (that is, the intentional ones rather than the wrecks) can be maintained with any desired depth of water over them and in just the spot the fishermen prefer. They can be made out of virtually anything that is reasonaby solid and will not pollute the water—old street cars, concrete pipe, carefully stripped automobiles, building rubble, even old rubber tires. However, very few materials are chemically stable in sea water. Most metals corrode, and the products of this chemical activity are not always palatable to the fish. Some concrete also emits chemicals that seem to repel fish. On the whole, however, the sea life seems grateful for whatever they can use for attachment or shelter.

Within two years, an experimental reef created from about six old trolley cars off California had a population of several thousand fish of catchable size. In Hawaii a reef made of over 400 car bodies spectacularly increased the standing crop of fish. A large artificial reef of building rubble off Long Island, known as the McAllister Grounds, has become a favorite rendezvous for sports fishermen. Another very large reef of building rubble exists off Niigata Prefecture, Japan, courtesy of an earthquake that destroyed many buildings that had to be cleared away. Still another reef, off Fire Island, New York, was created out of thousands of beer cases weighted with cement blocks.

Unfortunately, success will not necessarily follow every time a load of more or less durable junk is dumped overboard. Artificial reefs have been known to be covered over by silt and to be scattered by storm surges. Much remains to be learned about the factors, environmental as well as structural, that are most effective in establishing colonies of fish.

Obviously an underwater structure that will house humans is more exciting and more novel, than one, like an artificial reef that houses fish. *SeaLabs I, II,* and *III* and the various ocean habitats of Cousteau and Link are existing examples of human habitats. Repercussions from these experiments are already evident in a number of directions.

One such application bears the very appropriate acronym LOSS (*Large Object Salvage System*). LOSS, one of the interlocking ventures of the Deep Submergence Systems Group, is aimed at giving the United States the capability of recovering objects up to 1,000 tons in waters over the continental shelves. It incorporates surface support ships, personnel tranfer capsules that can take divers to and from the bottom at full ocean pressure, undersea habitats, navigation systems for the divers, methods for keeping them reasonably comfortable in icy and muddy waters, a multitude of acoustic communication links, and numerous special tools and salvage techniques. Many of these tools and equipments are still being developed. The long-term aim is nothing less than permanent possession of the ocean bottom.

Almost as an afterthought, the LOSS system includes an underwater habitat. One of its possible roles is as a temporary workshop on the bottom. There is plenty of room for development.

The dozen or so ocean habitats so far built have all been open to the sea. Therefore, except for the blessing of being out of the painfully cold water, free of the dangers of poisonous ocean plants and animals, and close to a hot meal, a shower, and a bed, their inhabitants continue to face all the difficulties and exasperations of life under a high-pressure atmosphere. Talking is difficult, sores won't heal, fried foods are out of the question (for frying creates contaminants hard to filter from the air), a kitchen fire is a tragedy. Electrical appliances won't work in the heavy helium atmosphere. Conventional overload devices on electric motors become unreliable. And there is always the problem of accurately controlling the synthetic atmosphere in which, as the depth increases, the permissible amounts of oxygen and CO_2 become difficult to control with currently available instrumentation.

Increasingly engineers are talking of underwater habitations that would be held at essentially atmospheric pressure, or at least at no greater pressure than afflicts a tourist gazing at the Dead Sea. This would enormously reduce the physical strain on the crew. It also brings up all the structural problems that face the designer of a submarine's pressure hull, plus a few more. If the men inside are to get out easily, or if those who are outside want to reenter, a "lock-out" chamber—that is a pressure, or air, lock—is necessary.

Any thought of sending divers in and out freely is futile. With some hazard, they could get out. But to come back, they would first have to spend many hours in a decompression chamber. Men brought to an atmospheric pressure habitat from the surface by submarine could enter if a watertight seal to a hatch on the submarine could be made. A crew about to be relieved could return in the same manner. But no popping in and out for a quick swim.

In shallow water it is easy to visualize a shaft emerging into the air, thus obviating the need for a self-contained life support system. As the water deepens, this shaft, exposed to currents and waves, becomes a massive and expensive structure. Steel igloos on the bottom have been proposed. The hemispherical form is optimum as far as resisting stress is concerned, but it remains to be demonstrated that a practical and dependable seal between the ocean bottom and the igloo is available. More likely, the underwater "cities" will wind up as a series of cramped, interconnected spheres.

It has been pointed out that many mines start on land and extend for thousands of feet under the sea. If the bedrock below bottom sediments were tunneled into deeply, so that thick layers of rock extended over the rooms that were excavated, large living spaces could be opened up that could be occupied in a more or less "shirt-sleeve" environment, if that phrase is used loosely, as if in respect to an expedition wintering over in Antarctica. Air could be supplied by gas generators brought down into the excavated areas. Or a shaft could be erected from the bedrock up to the ocean surface. Under the code name "Rock Site," this concept has been given a preliminary investigation by one of the U.S. Navy laboratories. The large amount of rock requiring removal would hopefully present a routine problem once a shaft to the surface was in place. The energy demands implicit in keeping a livable environment in such hostile circumstances require, as do so many other projects on the sea bottom, a nuclear power plant—and the whole thing works only if the rock walls and ceilings are thick enough and can be kept tight enough to bar entry of the high-pressure ocean outside.

In view of the size of many underground excavations that already exist, the hopes of the investigators that such projects could become permanently inhabited communities containing many hundreds and perhaps thousands of people are not beyond reality. It is at least as likely as a colony of equivalent size on Mars. Still, it will take a great deal of dedication on the part of the inhabitants, or, if you will, the crew. Living under the sea at sea-level pressure is an order of magnitude safer and more comfortable than living at the pressure of the ocean bottom. It is more like a very lengthy patrol in a submarine (something that tens of thousands of carefully selected and trained men have accomplished) than like a stay in a pressurized underwater habitat. However, neither a submarine nor an ocean-floor station is soon likely to rival the Caribe Hilton in comfort.

As of the moment, no underwater mineral deposit worthy of such an effort is known. Or to reverse the statement, present ocean technology is not yet capable of exploiting any known mineral deposit in deep water at a profit. Today's sulfur mines and the dredging for tin, diamonds, and gold operate generally at depths of less than a hundred feet. It would take an outlandishly rich mineral deposit and a very well-heeled mining company to establish an industrial habitat in really deep water.

The colonizing of the ocean floor is tangled with political, legal and technical traps. It is hard to predict when, or if, some overpowering national need or conviction will result in action.

When Truman first proclaimed the United States' prime right to its adjoining continental shelves, then and still un-cataloged, few gave more regard to his vision than the people of Lincoln's era gave to Seward's purchase of Alaska. It is far from inconceivable that, in some future international scramble for still deeper waters, the nation that first takes possession will best be able to demonstrate ownership. As this book goes to press, one immediate focus is the Cobb sea mount, an ancient volcano whose top rises to almost 100 feet from the ocean surface. It is about 270 miles off the state of Washington—beyond the territorial waters of the United States, and beyond the continental shelf. Plans are underway to establish a manned habitat on this oceanic pinnacle in the early seventies.

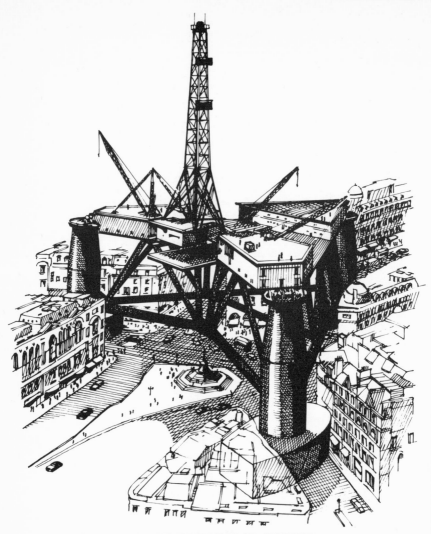

MOBILE DRILLING PLATFORM

This is an oil-well platform, of the mobile or floating type, as it would look if it were set down in Piccadilly Circus, in London. The huge "shoes" or pontoons at the bottom of the three columnar legs are an attempt to obtain a large bearing surface on soft or shifting bottoms. Wherever the water is shallow enough, such mobile platforms are flooded until they sink to the bottom. When the derrick picks up a string of drill casings, it must support up to a million pounds. Such platforms are heavier than many ships and cost up to $10 million per unit.

Fish in a Barrel

*In the year 1690 some persons were on a high hill ob-
serving the whales spouting and sporting with each
other, when one observed; there—pointing to the sea—
is a green pasture where our children's grandchildren
will go for bread.*
—OBED MACY's History of Nantucket (*Supplied by a
Sub-Sub Librarian whose name was Melville*)

ABOUT 1960 Iceland became so alarmed by competition
from foreign fishermen on her rich offshore grounds that
she extended her limit of national control to twelve miles
from her coasts. British fishermen, who had worked these
grounds for centuries, resisted eviction, and a British warship appeared upon the scene. For a few days it appeared
that war was about to break out over an issue not much
bigger than a few herring to the world at large but life or
death to a nation supported only by her fishing fleet.*

On October 17, 1966, the President of the United States
signed a bill without precedent in the history of this republic,
extending the United States zone of exclusive fishing to twelve
miles off the coast. The story appeared on the bottom of
page sixteen of *The New York Times,* sharing the column
with two other legislative items from Washington. Late in
November 1967 the United States announced that a bilateral

* Fish and fish products account for 95 percent of Iceland's exports.

treaty had been signed with the Soviet Union in which Russia agreed, in return for certain concessions, not to fish for three months of the year in a critical area lying south of New England in which heavy schooling of certain food fish occur. Because of the sharp reduction that had occurred in the catch of these species, both the United States and Russia thought it to their mutual benefit to give the stock a chance to recover.

The inhabitants of the United States are among the few of this world who, by and large, have too much to eat. People can starve in the United States, too, but not because of general famine. This is the nation of diet-watcher clubs and not-foods, preparations whose advertised virtues are that they taste and look like food but won't really nourish one. The idea of enjoying the pleasures of the table while avoiding the medical consequences of gluttony will undoubtedly appeal to the more hedonistic of the world's hungry peoples as an intriguing if unattainable perversity. But the concept of low-calorie dog food, which this country also manufactures, would surely stun the hundreds of millions who regard a plump dog as a delectable morsel.

It follows that the United States is not the ideal audience to address on the subject of the oceans as a food reservoir. The neglect we afford our own fishing industry is a case in point. Whereas the investment of American dollars and American know-how in foreign-based fishing fleets is large and growing, our own per capita consumption of fish has been relatively trendless for the past thirty years—this while the world's catch has been growing steadily, in some years several times faster than the world's population. This is the only major food source with even remotely that kind of momentum. Peru, Japan, China, and the Soviet Union are the largest fishing nations. In 1966 the United States dropped from fifth to sixth place.

Not that the total catch landed by American fishermen is small. Although it fluctuates sharply from year to year, as does the output of any hunting operation, it has grown to average several billion pounds per year, giving this country a per capita consumption twice that of the world as a whole— that is, statistically. Most of the catch is eaten by chickens, turkeys, and household pets. Much of the fish the people eat is imported.

The world's catch of fish and shellfish has seen extraordinary growth in this century. This rapid expansion was in full swing long before oceanography, let alone ocean technology, became a glamorous discipline. The world's fish catch, which amounted to about four million tons in 1900, was sixty million tons in 1966. Some of this increase is being sold by the larger fishing nations, particularly Russia, to protein-deficient areas of Africa and Asia, which never before have had significant supplies of fresh or frozen fish. This is helping these emerging have-nots nutritionally; it is also turning a profit for the selling nation, a foreign-aid procedure that would seem more constructive than giving the food away.

Sixty million tons is the proverbial drop in the bucket compared with the biological matter that is generated yearly in the oceans. How much that really amounts to, biologists can only estimate. The uncertainty in that estimate is probably larger than the world's yearly fish catch. For the sake of stating a number, it has been alleged that about 2 billion tons of animal matter big enough and of a quality at least potentially useful to man is formed in the ocean every year. The amount of plant matter formed—that is, the tiny algae and photoplankton that support the rest of the ocean economy—may be ten or more times greater still.

In very round numbers, it takes about one hundred pounds of photoplankton, the grass of the sea, to create ten pounds of zooplankton, the tiny herbivores that graze on the single-cell photoplankton. And it takes all ten pounds of this zooplankton to produce one pound of herring, a relatively decently tasting carnivore. As for larger and more desirable fish further up the chain, like salmon or swordfish, only ounces of these result from the original one hundred pounds of plant matter.

For many reasons, it does not necessarily follow that the world's fish catch will grow much faster in the immediate future than it has in the immediate past merely because helicopters, sonars, electronic lures, and other technically sophisticated devices are turned loose on the fish. Many of the older fishing grounds and at least one recently discovered area (that of Peru) are probably being fished near their limit already. That is, the largest sustainable yield, as the biologists put it, is already being taken. This is not an easy thing to prove, particularly to a professional fisherman. The biologists have no exact count of, let us say, all the anchovies in the sea, nor of the rate at which they produce, nor of the natural forces that (sometimes more than the fishing take) control the number available.

In the case of some large ocean animals, however, where an accurate estimate of population can be made and where birth rates and survivability are fairly well-known, the predictions of the biologists are proving all too dismally true. This is strikingly so for the great whales. Many species of seals would also be strikingly vulnerable to extinction by current hunting techniques if they had not already been driven into economic extinction. That is, they have become so scarce that it doesn't pay to hunt them any more.

If it is true that many of the older fishing grounds are being fished close to their limits, at least as far as currently acceptable species are concerned, increased production must come from new grounds (which are still being found) or from the catching of new species. Because dietary customs tend to be rock hard and to change almost as slowly as religions, the finding of an abundant new and edible species does not necessarily put food into anyone's mouth. At least, not directly.

Fishing is of course a form of hunting, in which the hunter takes his turn at the harvest after the angel of death has taken the first 99.9 percent or perhaps 99.99 percent of the young fry. In a recent experiment in England, which involved the temporary damming of a small arm of the sea, then seeding it with plaice eggs, some 300,000 young plaice were soon swimming around. But when these animals were exposed to open sea conditions, about two-thirds of them were eaten by eels and crabs within a matter of a few weeks. What is even more galling is that, once in the open sea, fish, who show neither gratitude nor patriotism, are as willing to be taken by a foreign fisherman as by the nation that took care of them while they were young.

For many reasons, fishing is even a more inefficient process as compared to fish farming than hunting is to animal husbandry. However, after some 5,000–10,000 years of trying, we know how to raise cows, pigs, and chickens quite effectively. We have bred strains that have the qualities we desire rather than the qualities that would help them survive best without man's protection. Milk and egg yields, for example, have been raised by a factor of almost a hundred as compared to the wild strains. We grow turkeys with lots of white meat, and square-shaped Angus cattle. We know how to protect the herds and flocks from epidemic disease, what cheap foods will keep them fat and healthy, what climates each breed likes best.

As much could be done with fish breeding, as a relatively few experiments have already shown. But fish farming and fish breeding are relatively embryonic arts. The Japanese, with 300 years' experience, have been at it longer than virtually anyone (except perhaps the Chinese). In Japan, about 10 percent of the total catch (money value) comes from cultivated stretches of fresh or salt water. Most of this output is very much in the luxury class. Pearls for the jewelry trade and oysters for the gourmet, so to speak. The edible mollusks are grown on long ropes suspended from surface buoys so that they can use the full three-dimentional volume of the ocean rather than just the bottom area. The Japanese have recently reported some success in raising that delicate and unpredictable creature—the shrimp.

In the United States selective breeding of rainbow trout over a period of about thirty-five years resulted in fish that, given enough food, can weigh fifteen pounds at two years, an age when their wild cousins weigh an average of only a few ounces. By similar techniques larger, stronger, and faster breeding salmon have been produced.

Where it concerns the ocean, fish farming may become as much a matter of massive engineering as it is of ocean biology. The conditions in a small lake can be controlled fairly well. Damming a large estuary or arm of the sea involves considerations aside from the need for large sums of money. It has effects on navigation, on pollution control, on the habits of migrating animals, on the temperature and climate of the area, on tides and currents, and on the kinds of erosion these will henceforth create. Large-scale fish farming, requiring major structural alterations of sea coasts, can be said to be as yet in an experimental and conceptual state.

Such attempts as have been made to dam off parts of the sea, as in Holland, have been for the purpose of reclaiming land for farming. Proposals are arising, however, for controlling small ocean areas. The suggestion has been made in the United States to cut off Long Island Sound at either end—not, however, to raise fish for affluent Long Islanders. The objective is to create large sources of fresh water close to areas that are beginning to experience chronic shortages in this basic resource.

Whether one farms or fishes, a statement that one can obtain ten times the yield from a given area under controlled conditions (as has been demonstrated) is economically meaningless unless equated to the money, labor, and resources that must be allocated to make this possible. Except locally and for very high-priced delicacies, a greater return in fish can still be obtained by resorting to the open sea than by farming. How long this will be the case depends in part on how many more good fishing grounds remain to be discovered and how hungry people get.

One factor that favors fishing rather than farming is that the ocean supplies its own fertilizer, and fertilizer is what makes the farm go. The heavy fishing areas of the oceans are almost without exception areas of upwelling—regions where for one of several hydrodynamic reasons the cold, nutrient-rich waters of the great depths rise to the surface. This bottom water is cold because all bottom water is cold, made up of dense outflow from polar seas. Water from the abyss is rich in organic matter because there is not enough light and oxygen there to use it up. It is in the top thousand feet or so that most of the nutrients are converted, by the aid of the sun's energy, into living protoplasm.

Below this layer of photosynthesis, plankton becomes scarce and eventually all but disappears. But not quite. It had been thought that the abyssal fauna, the animals of the great depths, were kept going only by the rain of organic debris that sifts continually down from the surface layers. Much of the debris is not caught by the relatively sparse population of carnivores in the deep sea. The bacterial population is also scarce. Thus, most of the organic debris eventually dissociates into basic molecular complexes that are removed from the biological cycle for years or centuries until the slow circulation of the sea once more brings them to the surface.

It is not really quite that simple. Perhaps, in a few more years, it will look a lot more complicated. Although oceanographers have been taking deepwater samples since the *Challenger* expedition a century ago, the oceans are very large, and the few thousand analyses performed prior to World War II merely revealed a glimpse of the chemistry of the abyss. The much more intensive exploration with more sensitive instruments that has been underway since World War II is continually turning up surprises about what was thought to be a relatively dead world. A recent one is that in every liter of virtually all deep waters that have been sampled there are thousands, sometimes hundreds of thousands, of tiny flagellated, single-cell creatures. Living at only a few degrees above the freezing point of fresh water, they nevertheless maintain metabolic activity, and without the aid of sunlight. They can apparently grow on the dissolved or particulate organic substances about them. Their existence had long been known, but it was not until 1965 that their concentration—about one hundred times what had been supposed—was accurately measured. It is a fair surmise that these tiny creatures are a source of food to the unexpectedly large concentration of deep-water copepods, the small, sometimes microscopic crustaceans that are one of the basic links in the oceanic food chain.

One of the more lively topics of debate at almost any oceanographic conference is the future world yield of fish. In view of the quite limited knowledge of the ocean's fishery resources and the inability to foretell what new innovation in fishing practice will prove practical, it's a real horse race, with the numbers quoted deriving as much from emotion as fact. Experts are guessing at between eighty million tons and 200 million tons per year for the total world catch in 1990. Other experts, known as demographers, attempting to prognosticate the world's future population, come up with an estimate of about five to six billion people in 1990. Thus even the optimists among the ichthyological experts (and what fisherman is a pessimist?) are estimating a catch of less than one hundred pounds of fish per year per capita, and this includes the huge amount that now go to animals and fertilizers. If we assume, still optimistically, that, on average, thirty pounds of cleaned fish proteins reaches every man, woman, and child each year, it amounts to less than two ounces per day.

This princely portion does not quite prevent the pessimists from experiencing a small shiver of doubt whenever a new and superior fishing technique is announced. Modern fishing boats have substituted power winches and hoists for human muscle. They can handle far larger nets and trawls than before, and in rougher water so that the fishing seasons can be extended. They can process and freeze the fish on board. They use helicopters, planes, radio communications, sonar, and bathythermography to help find the schools, with marked success. Soon, perhaps, underwater TV cameras will spot the fish, electronic lures or colored lights or chemicals will attract the exact species desired, and pumps will pull them aboard like so much gravel (such techniques are in experimental use today).

That is just the trouble. Man has demonstrated time and again that he can create killing tools that are not merely good, but too good. Only rarely has he shown the degree of restraint and international cooperation needed when one of these tools gets to be too much for a species. Time was when the North American continent supported forty million buffalo and several hundred thousand Indians living off them. Then came a few thousand white hunters with rifles, and the reign of the buffalo ended. Eskimo and caribou lived in equilibrium for millennia until the Eskimos got their hands on some rifles. Now the Canadian and United States governments are trying to teach the Eskimos how to raise reindeer even though Eskimos and reindeer have to date shown no remarkable degree of compatibility.

Or take the simple harpoon. Admittedly it was far less effective in killing whales than the gun-fired, explosive harpoon developed about the turn of this century. In the late 1500s, the Dutch, English, and Scandinavians, using hand harpoons, started to hunt the Atlantic right whale, so called because it was a large, fat, slow, easily killed creature quite different from the fast and powerful rorquals (the finbacks and sulfur bottoms) that were very definitely the wrong whales to pursue. In some years as many as 350 ships took part in these fisheries. Not until the early 1800s did the Europeans, with very little help from the Yankees, succeed in making this whale too scarce to hunt. In fact, until about a decade ago, it was thought that the Atlantic right whale had been exterminated.

The New Englander had no choice but to take off mostly after the sperm whale, a tougher and faster animal than the right. By the 1860s, and still using hand-hurled harpoons not basically different from their Stone Age counterparts, the Yankees had succeeded in making this whale scarce. Only the intervention of the Civil War and the subsequent discovery of oil in Pennsylvania, which for a time made whale hunting unprofitable, prevented them from exterminating it.

Until the explosive harpoon was mounted on fast power-driven whale ships, the very greatest and fastest of the whales, which live mostly around the perimeter of Antarctica, could not be taken. But mechanization ended this sanctuary and today all the great whales are under the threat of extinction. The blue whale, the largest animal that has ever existed on this planet, the finback, and humpbacks, which were not much smaller, have always existed in small populations. Probably there were never as many as a million blue whales in the world at any one time. Easy to find and few in number, they are particularly vulnerable to hunting pressure. Most commercial fish populations are more widely dispersed and far greater in numbers, yet it is still only a matter of degree. Given our unshakable enthusiasm for technological improvement, given enough fishing vessels, probably any species of interest to man can be overfished.

Some restraints do, of course, affect the industry, the most important being that the costs of fishing go up sharply as a species diminishes in numbers. This is demonstrated frequently as the various biological checks and balances cause a species to fluctuate radically from year to year. Nations do cooperate on occasion, a whole series of successful fishing pacts being among the evidence. And perhaps slowly the technical and financial problems of farming the sea will be overcome so that large and stable yields will be available.

Perhaps the saddest fact about overfishing is that it needlessly destroys a steady source of economic benefit. It has been estimated that were the Antarctic whales allowed to build up to their optimum population levels (if it is not already too late for even an enlightened international pact to make this possible), the area could supply 1.5 million tons of whale products indefinitely. At current prices that yield is worth $200 million, equivalent in capital invested at 10 percent return per year, to $2 billion.

Although we don't quite know where it is, there is a bottom to the barrel. What makes it even more confusing is that the barrel is not of constant size. If oceanographers or fishermen discover a new ground, the barrel gets deeper. So does it if people learn to like a new species of fish, start to farm fish on a large scale, or, better still, learn somehow to control large ocean areas so that desired fish are formed in place of unwanted organisms. We are not, however, going to increase the size of this barrel by better fishing techniques or by a sovereign insistence, in the face of expert testimony to the contrary, that there are plenty of fish left.

The Facts of Oceanographic Life

*The abyss in front of us is like planetary space, un-
known to the feet of man.*
—WILLIAM BEEHE (Log of the Sun, 1906)
*The spirit of mankind will never rest till every spot . . .
has been trodden by the foot of man, till every enigma
has been solved.*
—DR. FRIDTJOF NANSEN (Farthest North,
Harper & Bros., 1898)
*A time will come in later years when the Ocean will
unloose the bands of things, when the immeasurable
earth will lie open, when seafarers will discover new
countries, and Thule will no longer be the extreme
point among the lands.*
—SENECA (Lucius Annaeus, A.D. 63)

THE TIME HAS COME, and the foot of man is treading into
the abyss. However, venturers into the deep learn quickly that
the two worlds on this planet—the world of land and air
and the much greater world of salt water—are very different.
The entrepreneur, the naval officer, the engineer, the scientist,
the administrator of an ocean engineering program, the banker
who puts up the money—all must understand the basic facts
of life as they exist in the oceans if they are to maximize their
progress and minimize their frustrations. Like most basic
truths, these oceanographic facts are quite simple, even
obvious. What tends to be disconcerting are the consequences when they are ignored.

Take, for example, the first fact of life that affects ocean technology. The oceans are vast, almost incomprehensibly so. As every text on oceanography explains in the opening chapter, they occupy more than twice as much area as all the continents and islands of this planet put together. The continental shelves alone, are equivalent in size to a large continent, one approximately as large as Africa. There is more continental shelf off New Jersey than there is New Jersey. One consequence of sheer size is that finding something can take an exasperating amount of time. And "time," says an inexorable economic law, "is money." Generally, a man in a dense fog on land can search faster than a diver in deep water. Except perhaps when searching for oil with powerful acoustic waves, all other searches—magnetic, optical, and so on—tend to go far more slowly than on land.

And suppose that one does eventually find the ore deposit or the wrecked galleon. The featureless and almost infinite surface of the ocean offers no convenient landmarks. They must be supplied, not by the stars, which yield too vague a position, but by acoustic markers placed on the bottom by divers or submarines.

Which brings us to our next fact of life. The oceans are salty. Naturally, says the reader, everyone knows that. What it means to the designer—in one engineer's words—is that everything he builds has to operate in a fluid as corrosive as dilute sulfuric acid. Not only does this limit the materials he can use; even these he must pair in very restricted fashion or be faced with the added problems of galvanic corrosion. Salt water is an electrolyte that with the right—or, as it generally turns out, the wrong—combination of metals can help make a very effective battery. This is fine if one is designing an electric battery. But a ship that turns out also to be a battery means added business for the repair yards.

What is worse than its corrosive properties is that salt water, because it is a conductor of electricity, cannot be penetrated for any significant distance by radio waves or radar and not very much farther by visible light. For man to "see" or to communicate at a distance in the oceans is a generally costly and uncertain procedure, carried out by methods that would be cause for derision on land.

A third and onerous fact is the pressure that builds up rapidly as one descends into the sea, and at a rate that air-bound creatures can comprehend only in the abstract terms of mathematics. In the ocean pressures rise about one atmosphere (14.7 pounds per square inch) for every thirty-three feet of depth. At 13,000 feet (and about half the ocean bottom lies *below* that depth) the pressure is almost three tons (actually 5,800 pounds) per square inch. The pressure hull of a submarine at 13,000 feet must resist a force equivalent to the weight of a Cadillac concentrated on each square inch of surface.

The pressure goes up fast because sea water is dense— sixty-four pounds per cubic foot. This is almost 1,000 times denser than air at sea level. On the one hand this density is an aid to sound conduction, one of the relatively good means of communication in the sea. On the other it is an iron constraint on speed, so that in this vast domain, we must go about much more slowly than on, let alone over, land.

Even low-velocity currents can cause a variety of troublesome consequences on the bottom. To understand why a free diver has trouble standing up in a current of one and a half knots we need only translate that velocity into the pressure it exerts on anything in its path. Hydrodynamicists refer to the maximum pressure exerted on a unit area by a moving fluid as the stagnation pressure, $\frac{1}{2}\rho V^2$ where ρ is the density and V is the velocity. What it boils down to is that a one-and-one-half-knot current of sea water pushes just as hard on a man as a fifty-mile-per-hour wind. A two-knot current pushes with hurricane force—the equivalent of close to ninety miles per hour.

A submarine on the bottom is in the same predicament. Unless it can actually anchor itself to the bottom it cannot guarantee that it will remain in one place. One might think that it could "flood negative," that is, fill its ballast tanks so that it weighed more than the water it displaced. However, few submarine designs permit the degree of negative buoyancy required to give even reasonable assurance of resisting the thrust of a water current, certainly not on the smooth sand or mud bottoms that are virtually the only safe ones to sit down on. One of the author's minor hobbies is cross-examining submarine skippers who have performed the fairly rare maneuver of putting their submarine on the bottom. All have reported that they have slid with tide and current, sometimes thousands of yards in a few hours.

Finally—and, so to speak, the ultimate fact—the oceans contain no free oxygen. There is a little in solution, enough so that a fish equipped with gills can maintain a sluggish existence. But a large, vigorous mammal, like man, must bring his atmosphere with him. Only when the designers of diving equipment or of the life-support systems of submarines calculate the pressure-tank capacity they require do they begin to realize how prodigally a human being uses oxygen when he is resting, let alone when he is working hard.

Internal-combustion engines, in fact, any engines that burn fuel, use air more prodigiously than does a human being, who after all is equivalent in his energy output to a fraction of a horsepower. Such engines simply cannot be used in sub-merged vehicles, which must thus be very slow and of limited endurance if they are cheap, and very expensive if they use an energy source (like a nuclear reactor) that can afford to ignore this particular fact of life.

Now for a more detailed look at the consequences, start-ing with communications. The efficiency and complexity of any group action, whether it be a pack of wolves on the hunt, or a group of scientists in the laboratory, depends upon the kind and amount of communication possible. A diver going down to assess the damage to a structure on the bottom is far more valuable to the engineers above him if he can tell them what he finds as he finds it. No amount of debriefing afterward is equivalent to "real time" communica-tion. A good many methods of underwater communication of reasonable practicality are available today if range is short. As range increases to a couple of miles, the methods become scarcer and less reliable.

When long-range communications are necessary between a group of men on land and the crew of a distant, submerged submarine, one set of radio frequencies works after a fashion—VLF and ULF, very low and ultralow frequency. Electro-magnetic law states that the attenuation of a signal goes up with the square of frequency. In a conductor like salt water the rate of attenuation is so high that the usual radio or radar wavelengths can penetrate distances measured only in inches or fractions of an inch. The very low and ultralow radio fre-quencies—those well below the standard broadcast band—can be received by a submarine when it is submerged down to scores and even hundreds of feet. But the enormous wave-lengths involved (in air, almost nineteen miles for a 100,000-

cycle-per-second frequency)* require tremendous antennas for efficiency and have prevented their use as a submarine detection device.

Navies use these frequencies—in the region of from three to thirty kilocycles—for worldwide communication with their submarine fleets. These broadcasting stations are among the most powerful in existence. The Russian station known as Goliath (it was built by the Germans to communicate with their U-boats) was believed to have an output of about 350,-000 kilowatts. The new Cutler station in Maine can put over 1,000,000 kilowatts into its antennas. That's about twenty times as much power as our largest commercial transmitters. In addition to the new station in Maine, we have similar stations in Oahu, the state of Washington, and the western tip of Australia.

As one goes to higher electromagnetic frequencies, he encounters in succession the far infrared, near infrared, visible light, ultraviolet, and then X rays and gamma radiations. Significantly, a partial window exists in the region of visible light, particularly at the green wavelengths. In bright sunlight over clear water and from the proper angle, a submarine 100 or 200 feet down can be seen by the naked eye of an observer in an aircraft.

Light has a frequency in the order of 10^{14}, that is, some 10,000 billion cycles per second. In other words, it has a very short wavelength. Its resolution and therefore its ability to demonstrate fine detail is far greater than that of any practically achievable sound waves. If one wants to see a

---

* As an acoustic parallel, a 10,000-cycle-per-second tone in water has a wavelength of about half a foot. Therefore, it can be focused and controlled by transducers or lenses of reasonable size.

one-inch bolt on an oil-well head rather than a 300-foot submarine, or a quarter-inch diamond rather than a sea mount, only light will do. In the terminology of information theory, a light beam has a huge capability to carry information because of its high carrier frequency. Getting information on and off a light beam—and conveying it more or less undisturbed through the turbulences and other nonhomogeneities of the air or water path—is, of course, another matter, one which can get rather complicated. Thus, the frequently heard statement that one laser beam could carry, simultaneously, all the country's TV programs. It is like the statements frequently seen during the 1920s and 1930s in Sunday supplements that the atomic energy in a glass of water could drive an ocean liner across the Atlantic. True, but how do you do it?

Because light waves do indeed have such high frequencies and therefore short wavelengths, they suffer, in water, far more than does acoustic energy from scattering and absorption. The absorption of light by the surrounding fluid is high, but it is not to be compared to the effects of scattering. Microscopic particles, of which the ocean is full, will reflect or refract light waves. Sonar will be seriously interfered with only by objects that are of significant size compared to an acoustic wavelength. Thus, a sonar beam with a frequency of 5,000 cycles per second, and therefore a wavelength of about a foot, will pass through a school of small fish (unless these are extraordinarily concentrated) with little scattering. On the other hand, a sonar with a frequency of 500,000 cycles per second will be seriously interfered with by plankton and other relatively small scatters in the water. This explains in part the erratic performance, as a function of sea conditions, that is characteristic of high-frequency, high-resolution sonars as compared to their lower-frequency cousins.

The rapid absorption and scattering of light in even the clearest waters is painfully evident to photographers, particularly at depths where that great free source of illumination, the sun, is no longer effective. A camera and light system about thirty feet above the bottom, making use of powerful flash lamps, may cover 500 square feet per photograph (about the area of a large living room). By comparison, an aerial photograph taken from a plane at 30,000 feet altitude can cover twenty square miles, the area of a city.

Although light sources more intense than the sun are now available, it is hard to beat that celestial furnace. At midday in clear air, the sun can produce about 10,000 foot-candles on the ocean surface. This is equivalent to a power density of two watts per square meter, which is what stokes the entire biological economy of the sea. A full moon produces only 0.02 foot-candles. Starlight alone will produce 0.00008 foot-candles, yet there are television cameras so sensitive that they can record images using only starlight. Under the best of circumstances some natural light is present in ocean water to a depth of perhaps 2,000 feet. In the Sargasso Sea, which is about as clear as ocean water ever gets, a diver might see a large fish 100–200 feet away. As an extreme example, it has been reported that observers have been able to see a 900-pound Weddell seal 300 feet away by the light filtering through six feet of Antarctic ice. (Polar waters, at those seasons when they are not teeming with plankton, vie with the biologically deserted tropic seas in clarity.)

Objects that are not illuminated by the sun but must be seen with the aid of a searchlight cannot be clearly identified beyond a range of perhaps thirty or forty feet. An exact number is hard to state, because objects vary widely in this reflectivity and in the ease with which they can be distinguished from a hazy background.

To form a sharp image a lens, be it in a camera or in an eye, must use only direct or monopath radiation, that is, light that has not been reflected or seriously refracted on the way from object to image. In large part, lack of contrast, more than lack of illumination, prevents what we call good "seeing" in the ocean. What happens is not so much that the light energy is dissipated but that it travels by an infinity of paths. At the receiving point there can be quite enough energy to activate a film or the retina of an eye, but it will form only a fog of light.

By the time that light has traveled less than 1½ attenuation lengths, which in the clearest ocean waters is less than thirty yards, most of the light energy has been scattered. In twenty attenuation lengths, less than a millionth of the light energy is still direct or monopath. But pulse techniques are applied to the light transmission, that is, if we give up the idea of seeing an image but wish merely to communicate by codes, significantly longer ranges—perhaps a few thousand yards—may be obtainable.

One other property of the sea that contributes to this fog is bioluminescence, the light emitted in short flashes or steadily by a myriad of ocean-dwelling creatures. These scattered sources of light integrate to form a haze that neither the human eye nor the most complex assembly of synchronized flash lamps and gated video cameras can yet combat.

A detection technique of somewhat greater range than light is magnetics, although by definition it is effective only in looking for objects made of magnetic material—like a steel submarine—but not one of aluminum or glass-plastic laminate. If the object to be located is in fact man-made rather than a mountain of iron ore, the sensitivity required of the magnetometer is formidable.

The earth's magnetic field is in the order of 50,000 gammas, and it is constantly fluctuating because of lighting flashes and interactions with the sun's radiations. At a distance of 1,000 feet, a 1,500-ton submarine distorts the earth's magnetic field by only a few tenths of a gamma. Thus, to be effective the magnetometer must be sensitive at least to one part in several hundred thousand. Magnetometers of such sensitivity are available and are frequently brought into play in bottom searches for large iron masses. Unfortunately they are indifferent as to the origin of the mass. Such searches tend to turn up a surfeit of clues, for the ocean bottom is littered with ship wrecks and magnetic anomalies of geological origin.

For long-range communication, detection, and tracking, the method of choice is acoustics. Some years ago, when one of the naval laboratories was going through the turmoil that springs up periodically whenever some hope arises that, at last, a way of propagating electromagnetic waves underwater has been found, the saying became common that there are only two ways of detecting objects in the ocean: sound and unsound.

The ocean is indeed a good conductor of sound, much better than air. Sound waves travel, in sea water, at an average speed of over 4,900 feet per second, about five times faster than in air, and with much less attenuation. Not that such attenuation is negligible, as it is with radar waves. At 10,000 cycles per second, a representative sonar frequency, the attenuation is approximately 200 times greater than it is at X-band radar frequencies.

The ocean has been likened to a huge auditorium with

very bad acoustics. Some parts of the ocean, like Arctic waters covered with ice, can be very quiet, but the usual ocean environment contains a variety of noise sources. Not only do sounds travel farther then in air before they become attenuated; they can reflect off the ocean surface better than does light off a mirror. Over 99.9 percent of the sound energy striking the water-air interface is reflected back. The bottom can also reflect, but with far less efficiency—the softer and muddier the bottom, the more sound energy is absorbed.

Because of noise caused by surface waves, water currents, marine animals, and distant ship traffic, the average noise level can be equivalent, in terms of sound pressure per unit area, to that of a busy office. But the acoustic characteristics of the ocean have an enormous range. Some parts of the ocean are quieter than the proverbial graveyard.

To a visually oriented animal, perhaps the most disconcerting aspect of sound propagation in the ocean is that sound waves rarely travel in straight lines. The ocean is full of temperature gradients. Because the velocity of sound varies sensitively with water temperature, sound paths are always bending as they move through the ocean's layers. Add to that the frequent reflections from surface and bottom, and determining what direction a sound really came from gets to be a job for a computer (or a large-brained porpoise).

Sometimes, when the refraction or bending of the sound waves is extreme, there will be dead zones that the sound cannot penetrate, though it can be heard far beyond these areas. There are channels in which the sound waves can be trapped and travel with astoundingly little loss of energy for thousands of miles. One such channel is about 2,400 feet deep (in some oceans) and use of it is made in location equipment for shipwrecked sailors or aviators. The Lamont Geological Observatory has exploded charges of TNT south of Australia and picked up the sound 233 minutes later and 12,000 miles away near Bermuda.

This brings up what is perhaps the most important aspect of oceanography to both pro- and antisubmarine operations and to any search procedure using sonar—the complicated way in which sound is propagated through the many-layered and ever-changing sea. The surface of the sea is in rough equilibrium with the air temperatures above it. If winds and sea states are high, as they are in the North Atlantic in winter, wave action keeps the upper layer well churned up and isothermal, that is, of constant temperature, down to as much as 400 feet (and occasionally to greater depths). Below these levels the temperature characteristically starts to fall sharply and then at a lower rate to the very cold levels— about four degrees centigrade—that characterize the abyssal depths over the entire planet, whether we are dealing with a polar or an equatorial sea. The seas are so vast and the tem-perature-versus-depth profiles can have so many variations that few oceanographers care to generalize on the subject. Atlases of temperatures profiles in various areas and at the various seasons of the year are available.

Because it is difficult to generalize, sonar experts con-stantly talk about bathythermographs and sound-velocity profiles. A bathythermograph is a measurement of ocean temperature versus depth. Temperature is relatively easy to measure, and temperature changes cause about ten times as much variation in the speed of sound as do the changes in salinity and pressure commonly encountered. However, in-struments for the direct measurement of sound velocity are becoming increasingly inexpensive and reliable, and they describe the exact rather than the inferred sound-velocity profile.

The sounds themselves are sometimes surprisingly explicit even to a novice putting on earphones for the first time. Water rushing past the ship's bow, for example, sounds exactly as expected. But generally the transition from the noises picked up by the sonar transducers to unambiguous statements about the type, range, and bearing of the object originating or reflecting the sound is a painfully difficult one, with traps that even the wary and experienced listener cannot always avoid. Take, for example, the problem of deciding from what source a sound emanates. Is it random noise? Was it made by a fish? Does it come from a man-made device, and if so what is it? A surface ship? A submarine? Or its wake? A deliberately planted decoy? A navigation beacon on the ocean floor? A torpedo? If it sounds like a diesel, is the diesel driving a Danish submarine or an Icelandic trawler?

This is for sound propagated in a basically horizontal plane—the long dimension of the ocean. Sonars that direct their pings downward and bounce them off the bottom to obtain a measure of bottom depth are a special class known as depth sounders. Not only have they saved countless ships and submarines from grounding; to the oceanographer they were the first tool to reveal the extraordinary complexity of contour that marks the ocean bottom. And when the deep diving research submarine enabled the oceanographers to see for themselves, they learned that what the depth sounder showed was only a pale, smeared copy of the true relief.

The first significant series of deep-ocean soundings were taken by weighted line from the deck of the *Challenger* during its expedition of 1873-1876. For each sounding the ship had to lie to for hours. Only when the depth sounder was coupled to automatic printing devices and oceanographic ships began to come home with literally miles of recordings did the more massive topographical features of the oceans come to light.

They are sufficiently numerous so that navigation by means of "landmarks" on the ocean bottom is a definite possibility. The geology and the topography of the ocean bottom are such vast and detailed subjects that not even an adequate summary can be given here. But one must at least have an inkling of these issues to understand a major aspect of the submarine environment.

If a piece of "average" ocean were to be examined it would be about 12,000 to 15,000 feet deep, have a flat mud bottom, and be devoid of magnetic or gravitational anomalies. But relatively little such ocean exists. About 7 percent of the ocean is less than 600 feet deep, the approximate depth of the edge of the continental shelves. From the point of view of ocean commerce, mining, and salvage, it is more important than any other ocean area of equal size.

Only about 10 percent of the ocean is deeper than 18,000 feet. In other words, although the deepest known point in the ocean is almost 36,000 feet down, a vehicle that can descend to half that depth can cover 90 percent of the ocean bottom. That is why the world's builders of deep-diving submarines have a working depth of 20,000 feet as one of their major goals. To reach the remaining area will take a vehicle with twice as heavy a hull. Table 1 illustrates the situation in more detail.

TABLE I. ESTIMATED DISTRIBUTION OF OCEAN DEPTHS

Depth in Feet	Percentage of Ocean Bottom Above Specified Depth
1,000	8.5
2,000	10.5
6,000	15.9
12,000	34.5
18,000	90.0
21,000	99.0
35,800	100.0

Perhaps the single most extraordinary feature of the ocean bottom is the Mid-Atlantic Ridge, whose foothills and main cordilleras, to use surface terminology, occupy nearly a third of the area of the Atlantic Ocean. Once confused with the allegedly lost continent of Atlantis and now one of the primary exhibits bolstering the theory of continental drift (it lies almost midway between the present positions of Africa and Europe on the one hand and North and South America on the other), this mountain chain comes to the surface at Iceland, the Azores, St. Peter's and St. Paul's Rocks near the Equator, and farther to the south, at Ascension Island, St. Helena, and Tristan da Cunha. The very top of this ridge is marked by an almost continuous rift valley like those that form the Dead Sea and are prominent in East Africa.

The Mid-Pacific Rise, on the other hand, does not have the enormous extent or the sharp demarcation of its Atlantic counterpart. Instead, the dominant geological features of the Pacific Ocean are a series of great fracture zones, a scattering of smaller massifs, and, it is estimated, as many as 10,000 isolated sea mounts. Some of the long, straight fracture zones are bounded by cliffs over a mile high and indicate displacements of the earth's crust in a generally east-west direction of as much as 600 miles. There are also plains, such as those of the Bering and Chuckchee seas, which are monotonously flat.

Aside from such "visible" irregularities (at least to depth sounders), there are also many magnetic and gravitational anomalies, that is, areas where the value of the earth's magnetic field or the acceleration of gravity is different from what should be expected on the basis of the geographical position. Recent magnetic maps of the eastern Pacific indicate many almost regularly spaced magnetic anomalies, some with sharper gradients than those that exist about submarines. All these irregularities of terrain and magnetic field, and many others, such as the nature of the sediments on the bottom, are of interest to an undersea vehicle trying to locate itself or to determine what materials lie below the bottom.

To turn from the bottom to the top, the surface of the ocean is an interface between a gas and a far heavier liquid. The characteristics of that interface have determined the size and nature of the waves the winds can whip up and therefore the shapes and dimensions of surface ships. The difference between living on the interface and living below the interface is the difference between a swimmer and a diver—a ship and a submarine.

By no means an insignificant consequence of the submarine's ability to dive is the fact that it becomes independent of wave action, for even shallow submergence greatly attenuates the effects of roll and pitch. There are stories of submarines 300 feet down rolling thirty degrees as a typhoon raged overhead, but these are rare exceptions. The submerged submarine is the ideal conveyance for the traveler with a queasy stomach. In fact, until very recently, the submarine was the only vehicle on which could be mounted a gravitometer. Since, as Einstein pointed out, gravity and acceleration are identical and cannot be told apart, one could not make a precise determination of gravity while the instrument was mounted on a jiggily, accelerating base. The Dutch oceanographer F. A. Venine-Meinesz, who recognized the possibilities of the submarine in this connection in the 1930s, achieved considerable fame prior to World War II by measuring the extreme gravitational anomalies in the chasms around the East Indies from a Dutch submarine.

The surface ship, however, must accept the wave conditions of the area and the season. During the winter in some parts of the North Atlantic, for example, sea states five or higher prevail as much as half the time. Sea state five involves wave heights from crest to trough of approximately ten feet and is described in the sailing manuals with considerable restraint as "very rough." Although fanatically stoic individuals have demonstrated that they can cross the Atlantic in a dinghy, the minimum size of vessel that can operate in such seas is generally over 1,000 tons displacement. In such seas most men aboard either feel ill or tire more quickly than usual. Operations that are simple on land, like hoisting a weight, let alone assembling an instrument, become difficult or impractical in heavy waves. "A broad search of Navy and Coast Guard records indicates that no ships less than 210 feet long operate continuously year in, year out, with more than 35 percent of their time at sea."*

Because the behavior of the ocean surface controls the design of surface ships' hydrofoils and air cushion vehicles in a profound way, and because waves are a major influence on

* "Market Time in the Gulf of Thailand," James A. Hodgman, Capt. U.S. Coast Guard, *Naval Review*, Frank Uhlig editor, U.S. Naval Institute, Annapolis, Maryland, 1968, p. 49.

the operation of radar and sonar, wave structure has been studied for decades. To date, theories of wave forms have of necessity been restricted to approximations that can be handled by available mathematical techniques. Actually, stereophotogrammetric pictures show the ocean surface to be a warped surface so complex as to defy mathematical description. Ordinarily, the sea is covered with both wind ripples, which are small, and gravity waves, which are the ones we ordinarily notice. The slope and height of these waves are nonlinear (not strictly proportional) functions of local wind speed, fetch (the distance over which the wind has traveled uninterrupted by land masses), and the past history of wind direction and velocity. Waves are almost never as steep as the human eye and the artist's brush tend to record them. A slope of over twenty degrees is extraordinary and is unstable. The stereophotogrammetric evidence is that four degrees is representative as an average slope and eight degrees is high.

Because the surface ship can float with most of its structure above water, it has less wetted area than a submarine of equivalent tonnage. At slow speeds, most of the energy required to drive a ship or submarine is spent in overcoming skin drag, and the submarine is at a disadvantage. But as speed increases, a larger and soon the dominant part of the propulsion energy of a surface ship is absorbed by the waves the hull generates. Soon the drag is going up faster than the square of the speed. An enormous effort has been made by naval architects to create hull forms, and particularly bow shapes, that will reduce wave making. It was the long, hollow bow lines that McKay introduced in his clippers that, more than any other factor, made those ships record breakers. Vehicles that are completely immersed in a fluid, like a dirigible or a submarine, face a radically different drag problem and as a result are radically different in shape.

Note that these are displacement hulls, not the planing hulls of small motorboats and some sail-driven craft, and not the hydrofoils, which "fly" with wings in the same manner as airplanes. To date, all ships large enough to keep to the open sea have had displacement hulls. In several nations, intensive investigation is underway on hydrofoils and air-cushion vehicles. To date, such craft have indicated their value in relatively short-range ferry and patrol operations. Much more will have to be learned of their stability, sea-keeping qualities, operating costs, and ultimate size capabilities before they have an assured place on transoceanic routes. Particularly for heavy loads, displacement hulls will be hard, so to speak, to displace. In terms of ton-miles per horsepower-hour, they are the most efficient load carriers known. No other vehicle, for example, has a higher lift-to-drag ratio than a large tanker.

To a man in a hurry, the most annoying aspect of a displacement hull is that its practical limit on speed goes up with the square root of the waterline length, explaining why, both for steam and sailing ships, the speed records have been set by the big ships.

A submarine of the size and displacement (approximately 2,000 tons) of the Guppy class begins to use less power when submerged than when on the surface at about eighteen knots. The cross-over point will vary with the design, but at any tonnage the point is eventually reached where the submerged hull can be driven faster and with less power than the surface hull. The limit on surface-ship speed is set by its wave making characteristics. For even 1,000-foot hulls this limit is in the region, practically, of about forty knots. However, the submarine is not rid of wave making until its hull is submerged at least several diameters.

The limit on the speed of a submerged vehicle is cavitation, a phenomenon encountered only in liquids. As Daniel Bernoulli pointed out in the eighteenth century, the pressure of a liquid falls as its velocity increases. As a body forces its way through a fluid there is a critical speed above which the pressure at some points on its surface drops sufficiently for the fluid to, in effect, boil, and bubbles of vapor result. The phenomenon generally occurs first on the tips of the propellers, which are always a sensitive part of a ship because they invariably have the highest relative speed. Severe cavitation can erode metal. Before the phenomenon was well understood there were cases of fast liners that could wear out a set of propellers during an Atlantic crossing. This phenomenon must be dismissed here after pointing out that the onset of full cavitation is marked by a sharp rise in drag and in flow noise. The drag increase is always important. So is the associated likelihood of damage to the metal structures in the area where the bubbles are collapsing. These bubbles make a great deal of noise as they collapse—no help to a military ship trying to tiptoe past an enemy. The greater the static pressure (the greater the depth), the faster a given shape can go before it cavitates.

Suffice it to say that the fastest torpedoes of World War II traveled at about forty-five knots and that torpedoes are not a great deal faster today. Submarines can already go almost that fast. With further refinement and a more lavish expenditure of power, there is little doubt that sustained speeds of about sixty knots can be reached by submerged vehicles, if desired. This is at relatively shallow depths—in the order of a few hundred feet. At greater depths, with the increasing static pressure of the ocean suppressing the onset of cavitation, still greater speeds are possible. In the end, it will become, as always, a balance between economic or military necessity, specific weight of the power plant (the usual matter of horsepower per pound), and costs.

Of course, there is no free oxygen in the water, so all the internal and external combustion systems that do so well in land and air vehicles must carry their own oxygen. The enormity of this penalty can be appraised from the fact that about four pounds of oxygen are required to burn one pound of an average hydrocarbon. What is worse, it is just about impractical to carry this oxygen around in its pure state, either as a compressed gas or a liquid. In either form oxygen is a bad customer. The problems that arise from the lack of free oxygen and from the expedients that must be taken to get around it are so different for diver and submarine, and so major, that they are treated separately in the next chapter.

Power Sources for the Abyss

Energy is the key to ocean exploration.
—E. E. FOWLER and NELSON F. SIEVERING, JR.,
U.S. Atomic Energy Commission

IF THERE IS ONE STATEMENT to which the entire underwater engineering fraternity will say, "Amen," it is that power is the lever that more than any other single factor will pry open the doors to the undersea world. Why should it be different for the ocean bottom than for the continental surfaces? Since the beginning of the industrial revolution, one of the central measures of productive efficiency has been the amount of power consumed per worker.

"From the hand-propelled *Turtle* of Revolutionary days," said Vice-Admiral Charles A. Lockwood, "to the nuclear propelled *Polaris* of today, the most important single item in a submarine's construction or equipment is propulsion." Today, except for nuclear-propelled submarines, every free underwater vehicle and every free diver is power starved.

The crew of a small battery-driven submarine worries constantly about the drain from every light bulb and every ventilating fan. In the blackness of the deeps, nothing will reassure and help more than light—kilowatts of light that cannot now be afforded except for brief flashes. Energy is needed to keep warm, far more energy than the diver can carry with him (until radioisotope sources become available). There is plenty of oxygen in the sea—if the water molecules are torn apart by electric currents to break the oxygen atoms free from the hydrogen. Cities under the sea are a fantasy until energy for light, heat, pumps, and tools is available. To date every manned habitat under the sea has had an umbilical cord leading to a nearby land station or surface vessel, where in a power plant with free access to the oxygen of the atmosphere has been generated the energy that made life below possible.

Power, in the world that is bathed by this planet's atmosphere, has become one of the cheapest ingredients of existence. In large blocks, power can be bought for a few pennies a kilowatt-hour. To produce the same amount of work—a kilowatt-hour—a strong man must sweat to the point of exhaustion for a day.

Except for the relatively few power sources that do not require oxygen (primarily hydroelectric and nuclear-reactor power), all our principal prime movers depend on burning fuel with oxygen obtained from the inexhaustible stores in the atmosphere. With free oxygen, engineers have produced a wide variety of cheap and efficient engines. In the United States, hardly anyone pushes a lawnmower today. It is so inexpensive to get a three- or four-horsepower engine. Few American automobiles now provide less than ninety horsepower. Three hundred or 400 horsepower in a vehicle that weighs less than three tons—the ratio for the world's prestige limousines—produces a more satisfactory pick-up. By contrast, the fifteen-ton *Alvin* obtains its power from two electric motors, each with a nominal rating of eleven horsepower.

Another benefit enjoyed by a power plant operating in air is low back pressure. The lower the back pressure, the higher the efficiency, which is why the airplane designer mutters when indignant citizens force him to muffle engine noise and, however slightly, raise the weight of the jet engine or the resistance of its tail pipe. Although a factory or a home using electric motors couldn't care less about back pressure, the electricity was produced in a power plant where the vacuum in the condensers was directly related to efficiency.

When that same designer attempts to select a power plant for a submarine, a torpedo, or a diver, he finds a ridiculous situation—enormous amounts of oxygen tied up chemically with hydrogen to form water, but—no free oxygen—and a back pressure that climbs rapidly with increasing depth. Some resolute inventors are suggesting various arrangements of artificial gills that will extract the oxygen that is dissolved in the sea water. For an application that requires the heavy expenditure of power, the area of membrane surface that must be exposed to oxygenated sea water becomes appalling.

The net result is that in spite of a century of effort, practical power sources for use underwater are few. Without exception they suffer from some technical or economic disadvantage, if systems built to operate in air are taken as the standard of reference. Today, electric batteries of the simple lead-acid type, such as are used in automobiles, power the bulk of the nonmilitary vehicles operating in the sea. Some military torpedoes still use internal-combustion engines that burn fuel in an oxidizer. These systems can deliver far more power than an equal weight of battery—at the expense of far more complications and limitations.

A small but growing number of radioisotope generators, virtually all of them of very low output, are being implanted in hard-to-get-at places. Most radioisotope generators so far built have delivered less than one hundred watts, and for this era few are envisioned that will create more than a few kilo-watts. This is what is required to run a kitchen for a house-wife who insists on simultaneously roasting a chicken, run-ning her mixer, and ironing a blouse. If she were asked to supply the several hundred thousand dollars necessary to buy a radioisotope generator of such size she would blow a fuse.

Fuel cells are being tried in a few vehicles and appear to be one of the more assured reasons why we may be on the threshold of a new era in underwater power. In spite of their current bulk and cost they have the potential to make a real dent in those applications that need power underwater for a week or two at a time.

Although fuel cells are not inherently restricted to pure oxygen and hydrogen as feeds, these are the gases for which the most highly developed cells exist. Storing large quantities of oxygen and hydrogen is not an appealing chore, but one to which hard-pressed designers of submarine power plants can become resigned. On land an armada of efforts are underway to make fuel cells operate on standard (or even nonstandard) hydrocarbons and on hydrogen peroxide or ordinary air as oxidizers. However, there should be little enthusiasm to store air, which is mostly nitrogen, in the cramped confines of a submarine, and the present fuel-cell cycle may very well remain the most favored.

In the orthodox fuel cell, a catalyst controls the union of hydrogen and oxygen at relatively low temperature so that the free energy of the reaction is released as direct current. The fuel cell's efficiency is very high—in the order of 70 percent when the power drain is low. The best stationary power plants, burning fuel under ideal conditions and using the most efficient turbogenerators available, do not much exceed 30 percent efficiency. Fuel cells for space craft were initially built in one- or two-kilowatt sizes, and few have yet exceeded (in 1969) ten kilowatts. However, there are no basic limitations on their maximum power output or length of operation.

Today's fuel cells are not yet small or light in any absolute sense. As this paragraph is being written, a two kilowatt fuel cell weighs approximately as much as a man and, exclusive of its fuel supply, occupies almost twice as much volume. (A 170-pound man displaces slightly less than three cubic feet.) Broad and energetic fuel-cell development programs are steadily chewing on these statistics.

Where large blocks of power are required for long periods, the nuclear reactor appears the unavoidable choice. The attack submarines such as were used by the hundreds in World War II required the power of a locomotive—up to several thousand horsepower. The much larger submarines of the current era require the power of several locomotives. This is small compared to the output of a central power station or the needs of a large mining operation, but given the limitations of the undersea world it is more than can be turned out by any other source of energy than a reactor.

The nuclear reactor is therefore achieving a monopoly in driving large submarines. The number in American, Russian, and British submarines (and soon, inevitably, in French, German, Japanese, and Red Chinese submarines) is approaching 200. For less urgent but still overwhelming reasons, nuclear reactors are driving (or soon will be) an increasing number of military surface vessels, icebreakers, and, quite probably, large, fast merchant ships on long hauls. All this will reduce the costs of producing and running nuclear reactors, but will not make them cheap.

To date, the nuclear reactor has been priced far out of

reach of the private or institutional user, at least as far as any known undersea project is concerned. By and large, the scientists or entrepreneur for whom the economic barriers have not been removed by military necessity or government insistence faces Hobson's choice in selecting his power source. Hobson, that celebrated owner of a London livery stable, allowed his clients to choose any horse they wanted of his large selection—as long as they picked the one in the end stall. The ocean engineer unblessed by a governmental nuclear-energy agency has until recently faced just as broad a selection: the electric battery.

Of all the power sources in wide use, the electric battery contains the least power per pound of weight. Otherwise, it has more virtues than a boy scout. Battery-driven vehicles are clean, quiet, reliable, simple, and relatively low in first cost. They need no oxygen. They could not care less about back pressure. They will not poison or blow up the pilot—if they are kept outside the pressure hull. They also limit the speed and endurance of any vehicle they power. No known type of battery, for example, can power a practical plane. It might get the plane off the ground, but then what?

The airplane power plant, in fact, epitomizes the ocean engineer's plight. A typical gas turbine on a standard jet plane—not a jumbo or a supersonic liner—develops a thrust of over 13,000 pounds. At 500 miles per hour, it is generating the equivalent of over 20,000 horsepower. Because the engine weighs less than 4,000 pounds, it manages to produce a horsepower for every four ounces of its weight. (A more sensational comparison, in terms of weight per horsepower, and one of even less significance, would be obtained by rating rocket engines in this manner.

For an underwater power plant, such statistics lose their sheen. The weight of fuel and oxygen that flows through a turbine, or for that matter, a piston engine, is immensely greater than the machinery weight. Invariably the oxidizer weighs more than the fuel. It is above all the weight of the oxidizer, at least four times the weight of the fuel, that prevents broad application of thermal plants to the undersea regime.

A standard four-engine jet, taking off from New York for a nonstop run to Paris or London, weighs in at well over 300,000 pounds as it starts its take-off run. (This is often more than its wheels can safely support in a landing.) A third of this gross weight is fuel. To a greater or lesser extent, all high-performance, long-range vehicles carry a large fraction of their weight in fuel. An ocean liner can, in one round trip across the North Atlantic, burn more than 10 percent of its not inconsiderable weight in fuel. And if it attempted a high-speed run on some of the longer routes of the Pacific, it wouldn't get there, for it would run out of fuel first.

Because oxygen rather than fuel is the prime necessity of these chemical heat engines and because the only free source, our atmosphere, also contains four times as much nitrogen as it does oxygen, air-breathing power plants use at least twenty tons of air with every ton of fuel. Perfect combustion is all but impossible when using just the chemically correct (stoichiometric) amount of oxygen; anything less than complete combustion of the fuel is wasteful, results in very hot gases that reduce engine life and contaminate the surroundings with a smoky exhaust. These engines almost invariably use an excess of air, sometimes several times as much as the minimum that is chemically sufficient. Thus, a commercial jet liner, flying from New York to Europe, can use over 1,000 tons of air in burning its load of fuel.

But a submarine can't use air from the atmosphere unless

it is snorkeling—that is, it has intake and exhaust pipes extending from the engine room to above the ocean surface. The snorkeling swimmer can submerge no more than about a foot below the surface. Similarly, the snorkeling submarine is confined to a thin skin of water scarcely sixty feet thick. This may have some military point, but is hardly of significance in deep-sea exploration.

With these facts in mind, let us see how the engineers have struggled with the power plants of the torpedo, whose relatively short run and freedom from economic restraints permits a wide choice of alternatives. In its military form, a torpedo operates for about fifteen minutes, perhaps at most, for half an hour. At its highest speed it needs several hundred horsepower (though these must be packed into a twenty-one-inch diameter).

The history of underwater propulsion is replete with early attempts to use exotic power plants. Electric torpedoes were powered by a cable unreeled from shore in 1871. Torpedoes with self-contained batteries were available by 1890. Rocket-propelled torpedoes were first investigated in the nineteenth century. A certain Bill Cunningham who was building rocket-propelled torpedoes for the U.S. Navy in 1893 caused some comment by firing one down a New Bedford street on the Fourth of July.

Today torpedoes rarely use conventional batteries, but rather expensive forms made in part of silver. Such batteries can contain up to four or five times as much power per pound as the lead-acid battery. Although the lead-acid cell is several times as heavy as a silver-cell battery, the lead-acid type can be recharged many times more frequently than can the silver cell. In addition there is a heavy initial cost to the latter, so that a battery big enough to drive a twenty-one-inch-diameter torpedo at military speeds can cost the equivalent of two well-appointed Cadillacs. As torpedoes run deeper, batteries become more attractive; that is, the designer runs out of effective alternatives. On the other hand, for shallower depths, and certainly for torpedoes intended to sink surface ships, thermal power plants (those burning fuel) produce higher speeds and longer ranges and continue to be used.

The point is of more than military interest. Robot vehicles are already in operation and are likely to be used widely in the future for underwater surveying, prospecting, and general reconnaissance. The history of the torpedo power plant is pertinent in understanding what can be properly expected from these robots.

Up to World War II, torpedoes were generally powered by storing compressed air in heavy steel cylinders that made up half the torpedo length, burning it with a hydrocarbon like alcohol or diesel oil, and passing the hot gases through either a small gas turbine or a reciprocating piston engine. These propulsion systems were deliberately wasteful of fuel. The aim of the designers was to achieve the lightest power plant and fuel package that would drive a torpedo at shallow depths for a small fraction of an hour. Nobody was interested in setting economy records. The World War II torpedoes of the United States, Great Britain, and Germany used, respectively, 19.5, 17.3, and 18.7 pounds of "expendables" per horsepower-hour. The expendables were the fuel (alcohol, kerosene, or decalin), the compressed air, and a little fresh water to keep the hot gases from melting down the engines. These torpedoes emitted an exhaust composed largely of gases not soluble in water. This was a real headache to the submarines that launched them, for an alert warship who sighted these wakes would sometimes charge down the torpedo track, from whose beginning the submarine could hardly be far removed.

Submarines and torpedoes have also run on pure oxygen. In the 1930s the navies of both the United States and Japan tried to run experimental torpedoes on compressed oxygen. Both Japan and the United States took casualties among their development personnel. The U.S. Navy became discouraged with this approach and, in essence, dropped it. The Japanese persevered, learned how to control the combustion process, and produced the famous "Long Lance" torpedoes that were without a doubt the most potent underwater weapons of World War II. Not until the 1960s could torpedoes of the Western nations match these "Long Lances" in speed and endurance.

These intricate propulsion systems had been designed in peacetime, when man-hours were not quite so difficult to obtain as they became under war conditions. The moral, as will be seen, holds for commercial or scientific vehicles also; dollars, whether they are expended on production or maintenance, equate to man-hours. Man-hours, particularly those of skilled people, are always in short supply. Ask any oceanographic institute suddenly afflicted with the gift of a deep submersible.

When the war came, the Germans already had under development a torpedo driven by electric batteries. It was, of course, slower and of less range than the chemically fueled types, but it was brute simple when compared to its cousins driven by thermal engines. It could be built in greater numbers by the same number of men, it left no wake, and it was quiet—a strong military advantage. The U.S. Navy indicated its agreement with the German position by shifting much of its torpedo production to electric propulsion, accepting, at the beginning, a loss of seventeen knots in speed as compared to the then-standard torpedoes.

In World War II the Germans started, once again, an abortive development of solid-fuel rockets for propelling torpedoes. Because of the extreme mismatch between the speed of the vehicle and the speed of the exhaust gases of a rocket, the efficiency was (and is) very poor. Because rockets run for seconds, or at best for a few minutes, range was short. This, rather than inefficiency, has been the bane of rocket engines underwater.

Submarines have never, except experimentally, used chemical heat engines when submerged. Basically that's because they have people aboard, and the crews don't seem to do well at frying-pan temperatures. Beginning in the 1890s, with the first practical submarines of Holland and Lake, gasoline and (later) diesel engines were used on the surface; electric batteries were used when submerged. It meant that the submarine had to carry two separate power systems, a harsh restriction.

This was the restraint until World War II. During that period the Germans experimented with two unconventional propulsion systems, neither of which had time to achieve operational use. These were the Walter and Erren cycles. Hellmuth G. Walter used concentrated hydrogen peroxide as the oxygen source. In a 3-percent solution, hydrogen peroxide is available in the drugstore for, among other purposes, the bleaching of hair. It can also be obtained in up to 90-percent concentration and must then be treated with considerable respect.

Several metals—notably platinum, nickel, and manganese —are catalysts that break down this compound into water and free oxygen. So are many organic compounds. If, for example, one tosses a cigar butt into a container of concentrated hydrogen peroxide or even spits in it, the oxygen can be released so fast and with so much heat that one can achieve an excellent low-order detonation. When a tank truck of the stuff lets go, and it has happened, it makes sufficient commotion so that public authorities take a considerable interest in how it is transported. Stabilized, highly concentrated hydrogen peroxide, in proper containers, is no more dangerous than gasoline, perhaps less so, but we are familiar with the evils of the latter and thus take them more lightly.

In the postwar period, both the United States and Great Britain built experimental submarines powered with hydrogen peroxide. One of them blew—well, actually there was an engine-room incident that lead to the installation of a diesel engine in place of the hydrogen peroxide power plant.

Erren, in Germany, took quite another track. When the submarine was on the surface, he used the submarine diesel engines conventionally to generate electricity. Instead of being stored in batteries, this electricity was used to hydrolyze water into its constituent elements, hydrogen and oxygen. Later, when the submarine was submerged, he injected these gases into that same diesel engine, its valves suitably modified, to obtain power. The exhaust is, of course, steam, easily condensed by the great volume of cold water around the submarine. Thus, he could run submerged without a tube reaching to the surface, without a wake, and without using up the air in the boat.

The scythe of the nuclear reactor has cut short the promise of both of these lines of development.

Many search and rescue submarines must be designed for

transport by air. This limits their weight to about thirty tons —at most forty. For work submarines and for many research submarines, transport to their operating areas is preferably by ship—still a severe limit on their overall weight. Some work submarines need sufficient endurance, a large enough crew, or so much heavy equipment that they are too big for plane or ship. These must now be towed to their operating area—a slow, uncomfortable, and sometimes risky procedure. It would be far preferable if these boats could get to their operating areas by themselves and be able to expend power more freely when on station. To submarines of any tonnage, the fuel cell now promises at least partial freedom from their present power-starved existence. To those larger submarines that can afford it, the nuclear reactor offers a complete, if twenty-four-carat-gold, solution.

For applications that require small amounts of power and that are not weight limited, the radioisotope generator can be used. As implied by their name, radioisotope generators, most of them with no moving parts and thus capable of extreme reliability, depend for their energy on the decay of the radioisotope element with which they are loaded. That the same element, at least in its chemical behavior, could exist with several different numbers of neutrons at its core, each a distinct isotope, was so subtle a physical truth that it was not known until 1907. Of the many thousands of known isotopes (there are of course only about one hundred elements) approximately 1,300 are radioactive. That is, they spontaneously decay by the emission of three kinds of radiation. Of these 1,300, about nine have a sufficient number of favorable characteristics to make them of interest as heat sources for practical sizes of generators. Nor are those nine particularly alike.

The Atomic Energy Commission has developed a series of Systems for Nuclear Auxiliary Power (SNAP). The even-numbered SNAP designs (they had reached the number 50 by 1965) are full-fledged but very light reactors. The odd-numbered SNAPs are radioisotope powered. SNAP 3 was demonstrated to President Eisenhower on January 16, 1959. It weighed four pounds and had a rated output of only 2.5 watts. The rated output of a device whose fuel is burning at a rate that can be neither turned off nor accelerated but that with time burns at a slower and slower pace is a difficult quantity to express. However, this little four-pound device could turn out 11,600 watt-hours of electricity in 280 days, at an *average* rate of about two watts (considerably more at the beginning, less at the end of the period). That was the equivalent of about 700 pounds of nickel-cadmium batteries. The comparison is superficial, for it assumes that the batteries would not be recharged. Only if a power plant were utterly inaccessible would one consider a device fueled with plutonium 238, as was the unit on the President's desk. Gold was then cheap and abundant by comparison.

The nine radioisotopes referred to above are cobalt 60, strontium 90, cesium 137, cerium 144, promethium 147, polonium 210, plutonium 238, curium 242, and curium 244. Very broadly they fall into two classes: those that require heavy shielding (the first four) and are, quite coincidentally, relatively cheap, and those that can be kept in much lighter containers but are, unfortunately, either rare or difficult to produce. Even for the more available isotopes, fuel is the most costly item in a radioisotope generator.

In their inevitable and unstoppable process of decay, radioisotopes emit alpha, beta, and gamma radiation. An alpha particle is the equivalent of a nucleus of a helium atom. Most alpha particles move so slowly that a thin, light shield can reduce their danger to safe levels. Even a heavy sheet of paper can produce a significant reduction in the radiation intensity. Beta rays are essentially electrons. Because they are light, the slower ones can be stopped quite easily. However, as they interact with the material slowing them down, the higher-speed beta rays produce secondary radiation of the same frequency as X rays.

These secondary emissions are called bremsstrahlung. Gamma radiation, like the bremsstrahlung, can be extremely penetrating and dangerous. Heavy shielding (in the SNAP series, up to 4 inches of lead or its equivalent) is required with radioisotopes that emit gamma rays or fast beta particles. Of all the substances that may be in a deep-submergence vehicle close to such a power source, biological tissue is the most sensitive and requires the most massive protection. Higher levels of radiation, but still far below what an unprotected source produces, will injure many electronic devices, particularly those that depend on the semiconductors' elements, as do transistors, rectifiers, and diodes.

Thus, a ten-watt generator capable of withstanding sea-water pressures to 10,000 pounds per square inch (a happy by-product of its heavy shield) weighs about 500 pounds (1965 technology). A fully shielded sixty-watt generator (six times as much power) might weigh 950 pounds. This is a characteristic of all nuclear-powered devices. The shield creates a threshold weight that severely penalizes units of small output if they are compared on a pounds per horsepower basis. Shield weights rise far less rapidly than power output, so that very large units tend to be the lightest in terms of pounds per horsepower.

Most radioisotope generators produce electricity by thermoelectric conversion. As materials capable of withstanding higher temperatures become more available, the more efficient thermionic converters may be used. With thermoelectric or thermionic conversion, the heat of the reactor is directly converted into electricity—quietly, without moving parts. But efficiency in 1968 was fairly low, rarely exceeding 10 percent.

For the big submarine and for the big surface ship, the near-term prospects are bright. Nuclear-fueled power plants are being built all over the world by the scores and hundreds, for they are becoming genuinely competitive with conventional steam plants even when the latter have access to cheap fossil fuels. That most of these nuclear plants are for stationary land installations is still a help to their use in the sea. The creation of a large production capability, fuel-recovery facilities, proven auxiliary components, and a broadly based technical know-how must inevitably reduce the cost of sea-going nuclear plants.

It is not only the submarine that will benefit. Studies for the U.S. Maritime Commission have demonstrated that for long, fast runs, freighters and passenger liners powered by uranium can show a greater financial return than those driven by conventional steam or diesel plants. As time has gone on, these analyses have shown, with increasing emphasis, that the United States government could actually reduce its shipping subsidies on many runs (the famous route 21 from the east coast of North America to the Far East is a prime example) by installing the initially more expensive nuclear reactors in new hulls.

When the number of possible types of fusion, of moderators, of nuclear fuels, of heat transfer fluids, of control, and of mechanical arrangement are considered, it becomes apparent that the art of designing nuclear power plants has a broad future.

What is all this energy needed for? With our limited imaginations we can only point to areas that are already under exploration. For the surface ship and the submarine, the main requirement is for propulsive energy so that high speed and long endurance can be cheaply obtained. For the underwater habitat power is needed for instrumentation and "hotel" loads, and in large amounts if industrial operations such as mining are required. Men must be kept warm; hot water is needed for laundry and showers. A little energy is even needed for cooking. With enough power, carbon dioxide can be scrubbed from the atmosphere; fresh water and oxygen can be generated from sea water.

As very compact energy sources become available, divers will be able to use power tools and heated suits routinely. When compact and long-lined energy sources are available at reasonable costs, acoustic beacons, seisomographs, navigation lights, weather stations, and oceanographic instrumentation will be used freely, not only in remote areas such as the Antarctic, Arctic, and deepest abyssal regions of the sea but also in the main sea lanes—to the great advantage of the maritime community.

Energy is not just the key to ocean exploration; it is the key to success to all major enterprises underwater.

The Smell of Money

*Now would I give a thousand furlongs of sea for an
acre of barren ground.* —The Tempest, Act I, Sc. I

Nᴏᴛ ᴀɴʏ ᴍᴏʀᴇ. The new land rush is toward the bottom
of the sea. And the lamp that lights the way is technology—
the lamp that calls up the genie who obeys every human
wish—regardless of the consequences. Sooner or later—and
for those problems that are technical and well defined, sooner
than later—solutions will be found. Are pressure hulls too
heavy? Is it a bit difficult to see through an inch of high-alloy
steel? Then let's build a sphere out of glass segments held together by a frame of titanium. Is the water too cold for diving?
Then give the diver his own radioisotope generator so that he
can keep warm and use power tools to boot. Is it hard for a
poor but worthy oceanographer to pack energy into his small
submarine? By 1975 inexpensive primary batteries delivering
several times as much power as present cells (or some still
better alternative) will be available.

It is necessary only to look at what has happened in the
past twenty-five years to realize that predictions about technical achievement must take into account the acceleration as
well as the current pace of scientific progress. The next
twenty-five years, let alone the next century, will bring about
astounding capabilities. What technology is likely to permit

in the undersea realm is much more than most engineers, including this one, are willing to concede over their signatures. Not only are they inhibited by a lifetime of professional caution; they simply lack sufficient prophetic power.

It does not require extraordinary *sang-froid,* however, to suggest that in another decade hundreds, if not thousands, of small submarines will be poking about the ocean floor; thousands, if not hundreds of thousands, of professional divers will be in action, spending hours rather than minutes on every dive.

The small personal submarine, privately maintained, is very close to actuality. For the time being it will probably be limited to continental-shelf depths and to excursions not too far from ports. Work submarines capable of reaching most of the ocean floor are already clearly within the technical or financial capability of many organizations and in many countries. Time can only multiply their availability.

At the moment, men can work in deep water and for long periods only by the technique of saturation diving. This requires rather massive equipment—decompression chambers, personnel transfer capsules, and so on—expensive but within the capability of most industrial nations. The great increase in output per diver permitted by saturation diving has sharply stimulated the industry. The wide use of an effective one-atmosphere suit would stimulate it even more sharply. It is not that this solution appeals by its elegance. The comfort and freedom it would give, the latitude it would permit in selecting divers, promise large gains in productivity. So many technical barriers confront the construction of a practical suit that few professional divers count on it for the near future. To couple a diver's suit with an exo-skeleton would seem to them an even more unlikely goal. But imagine a diver with serno-motors for muscles and bones of steel—a true master of the deep.

It is a fairly conservative prediction that before this century is out the world will see more nonmilitary submarines in action than military. And this is an era when the submarine has clearly become the key to naval supremacy. Basically, in betting against the march of technology one is doing something analogous to selling America short. The long odds are on technology.

The impact of many thousands of individuals, free to explore whatever cranny of the seas they can reach, cannot fail to be enormous. Such activity will subject every inch of the reachable ocean floor to the same minute, repeated scrutiny that has resulted, on land, in the discovery of the many resources that have stroked the industrial revolution. As of early 1968, all the world's nonmilitary submarines had made in the order of 7,000 dives and had spent less than 20,000 hours on the bottom. Either number is less than the generations of men who have spread out over this earth's deserts and caves, hills and valleys, scrutinizing and prying at every rock and leaf. Man now knows almost completely what lies on the surface of the land. When will he know as completely what lies on the floor of the ocean, let alone below it?

Will these individuals be permitted, however, to conduct such investigations? And even if they are not actively discouraged by local or international regulations, will any incentive of an economic nature be allowed?

These questions are not yet as acute as they will become. In spite of the oil wells, the fisheries, and the expanding fleets of tankers, man's approach to the sea is still in an era of exploration and survey. Although the last hundred years of oceanography, and particularly the last quarter century, have revealed an expanding succession of discoveries, their implications continue to outweigh their current impact. Some consequences are obvious. Marine transport, the absolute foundation for world trade and world prosperity, will continue to increase in efficiency, whether because of cargo submarines or better prediction of waves and wind, or better control over marine boring and fouling organisms, or, in-inevitably, because the greater the knowledge of the oceans the greater the power over them.

But how about a role for domesticated marine mammals —seals and small whales—as extensive as that for the dog, the horse, or even the cow? Or schools of supersalmon, grown and harvested in accordance with the fluctuating demands of the market? And preconditioned before they are released into the open sea to an acoustic signal, so that they will gather at the nets when their particular trumpet blows.

Such predictions are dreams untinged by fears and doubts because the undersea domain is still in an age of serendipity, of unexpected and happy discovery. In spite of the billions of dollars being invested in the offshore oil industry, the total industrial effort in the sea over the past generation remains trivial when compared to the construction in one year of new roads, buildings, and other facilities on land. The catalog of materials, mineral and organic, being extracted from the sea is impressive in length and rate of growth. But a similar catalog for the continents would quickly dwarf it. Furthermore, such activities as are being undertaken at sea are almost invariably in areas where territorial rights and claims have been clearly expressed.

In the wilder and deeper oceans, where no nation, at this writing, claims an absolute right, the work of the explorers has not yet brought controversy because their activities are at best exhilarating and at most neutral. The scientist does not disturb the environment, except microscopically. He will take one fish or a dozen, as specimens, but he will not exterminate the stock. He will drop dye in the water to study currents, but will not pollute an estuary with an unending Niagara of sewage and industrial waste.

Nevertheless, he is the trigger for a growing number of problems. It is not so much an occasional bizarre suggestion, like a proposal to dam Long Island Sound or to close the Bering Strait. Such ventures must be evaluated on a national and international scale, with the gains and losses whatever they may be, distributed among hundreds of millions of people. The real root of conflict lies in the growing realization of the maritime community (which includes the bulk of the world's population) that the seas contain riches beyond calculation. The smell of money is in the salt sea air—and more potent still, the smell of power for those who can command the deep.

Squabbles have already arisen. Most of them, fortunately, have been capable of settlement by national judicial structures (as when Texas, Louisiana, California, and most recently Maine quarreled with the federal government about the ownership of offshore acreage). A few cases, such as the division of the floor of the North Sea between the surrounding countries, have been settled (or remain to be settled) by international convention. Occasionally, but far from routinely, two or more countries will succeed in a treaty to modify fishing practices in the open sea.

Inevitably, however, as the prizes grow richer, the competition will grow in intensity. It is being suggested from many quarters that the great ocean basins, far from any country's shores, be placed under the jurisdiction of the United Nations. If the United Nations is indeed granted the right to auction or franchise ocean areas or to collect some tithe from the profits, it is conceivable, even likely, that in several generations the revenues from this Atlantis could make the United Nations a true superstate, capable of supporting armies that would make it a material as well as a moral power.

Initial reaction to this suggestion that the deep ocean floor be internationalized, from those powers actually capable of exploiting such areas, has been, privately, one of caution and even suspicion, for there is risk of great national injury in too enthusiastic an espousal of an international control system that will inevitably encounter unprecedented problems. Official positions have at worst indicated gingerly willingness to investigate the issue. This unavoidable agreement to talk will probably not slow a worldwide trend by maritime nations to claim more offshore territory by the extension or redefinition of territorial seas, fishery zones, and continental-shelf areas.

A slow-motion rush to stake claims is in progress, obscured by stately protocol and diplomatic phrases. Russia is increasingly restrictive about foreign fisheries on her continental shelves (and other nations about Russia). France insists it maintains a three-mile limit but bases it on a series of straight baselines that include some offshore islands. Her new three-mile limit is now in spots more than a score of miles seaward of her old three-mile limit. That is quite modest compared to the claims of most maritime nations of South America, or even of Norway.

Until some rule of law is agreed upon, the ocean floors beyond the continental shelves, more than half the area of the planet, belong to no one and contain no legal barriers to a head-on confrontation between rival claimants. "To be profitable," says Herman Pollack, of the U.S. State Department, "ocean exploration must be peaceful." However, some decades after Columbus revealed the New World to an astonished Europe and it had become clear that here was the Earth's greatest bonanza, a series of wars broke out between Spain, England, France, and some less powerful claimants that lasted about two centuries. Other wars that erupted after the discovery of valuable minerals in areas previously thought to contain nothing more than desert brush have involved just about every major country in the world, including the United States.

Perhaps the world is now more civilized, or urbane, or, possibly, convinced that a display of economic muscle is more profitable than the use of military might. But unless lions have in the meantime learned to lie down with lambs, some uneasy moments can be expected when an advancing undersea technology meets the first large and exploitable ore body some miles below the ocean surface.

In the beginning the sea had only two functions—as a broad highway between nations and as an inexhaustible source of fish that fishermen in their tiny and short-range craft could hardly scratch at. That was when the concept of *res communis* developed—that the sea was a realm held in common by the world except for a narrow strip near shore, which a nation could command with a cannon shot (whose range was the origin of the three-mile limit). As the range of shore-based artillery increased and as the very concept of range has been obliterated by world-spanning missiles, the United States and Great Britain continue to cling to this tradition, for it gives their merchant and military navies the right to go, unchallenged, anywhere except in the narrowest straits. Now, however, as more and more fishing grounds give evidence of overexploitation and as food becomes a more important tool of national policy, many countries are beginning to move out their fishing limits. Some insist as they do so that no precedents to undermine the three-mile limit on open navigation are being set. Others want absolute control. Russia, who has in the past supported a far more expansive attitude toward the width of national waters, is building up an international merchant fleet and navy as rapidly as possible. As she does, internal struggles over conflicting requirements for a law of the sea must mount for her as they have for the United States.

Today the ownership of the submarine realm is being debated. Tomorrow it may be fought over. Powering this competition is the pressure of a world population that is expanding at the rate of over a million human beings each week. Every year a population greater than that of France is being distributed among the world's nations. Yet the sea does not hold our salvation. It is vast but not limitless. Although the biological system of the oceans is enormous and has great inertia against disturbance and although it can and will provide far more than it has, the speed with which the world's population is growing guarantees that no long-term solution to world hunger is to be found in the gathering of naturally grown fish and shellfish. Nor is the panacea in fish farming, however thoroughly it shows that it can compete in terms of yield per acre with any kind of land agriculture. To farm economically an ocean, rather than a small pond, requires equipment and technology that, some say, will take another thirty to fifty years to develop. But that is not the basic problem. These salty fields will flourish to their maximum only under a degree of international cooperation as yet is not in sight. The most desperately needed inventions are those in international law.

As humanity increases its numbers, the wastes of industrial civilization—astounding in quantity and, sometimes, almost eternal in longevity—can no longer be left to the biological cycle to dispose of. As the consequences become visible, there is increasing opposition to dumping on land or in lakes and rivers. But the world ocean is still *res communis*. No one yet has the right to post a "No Dumping" sign on the high seas. Bottles, cans, paper and snarls of cable already litter every ocean floor that has been inspected. An inevitable world shift to nuclear power in the coming generation will create radioactive wastes in quantities hardly dreamed of a few years ago. The production of every 1,000 megawatts of electric power must produce an inevitable poundage of poisonous fission products. Although the natural radioactivity of the sea is far lower than that on land— actually less than 1/50 of what is experienced by people living over sedimentary rocks or granite—decades of gross indifference could result in contamination that is a direct danger to man. Because biological tissue can concentrate radioactivity to an extreme degree, such a rise could be in some cases a conservative estimate. The accidental contamination of fisheries has already been accomplished.

Nevertheless, however inevitable its problems and limitations, the submarine realm is the last great area left to explore on this planet. Pristine, enormous, it is a challenge to the inborn needs of man to discover, to invent, to overcome obstacles. At best it represents an opportunity to obtain an increment of food and materials that could lay the material foundation for a golden age embracing whole continents rather than a few fortunate countries. At the least it presents a new chance to gain time in which to hunt for more lasting solutions to the material ills that have so far been the heritage of man. Man does not live by bread alone, but until he has bread, he can live for nothing else.

INDEX

Index

NOTES ON ENDPAPERS

1. *Trieste*—one of the first of the bathyscaphs, launched in Trieste in 1953 and purchased by the U.S. Office of Naval Research in 1958. Described even by its users as primarily an elevator, it nevertheless demonstrated that the entire ocean was open to exploration in free vehicles. The silhouette shown here is of the now-defunct *Trieste I* rather than of the improved second version, *Trieste II*.

2. The *Diving Saucer (La Soucoupe Plongeant)*—Cousteau's brilliant first exercise in the practicality of small-submarine operation. Launched in 1959, this tiny hull demonstrated that men could explore the seas at a cost that even private organizations could afford.

3. *Alvin*—the first all-American entry into the research-submarine field. Funded by the U.S. Navy and operated by Woods Hole Oceanographic Institution, it has a 6,500-foot limit and has already repaid many times over its initial cost of less than $1 million.

4. *Aluminaut*—an innovation in hull materials. One of its key architects was Dr. Edward Wenk, later chairman of the National Council on Marine Resources and Engineering Development.

5. *Yomiuri*—one of the first of the Japanese research submarines, was financed by a newspaper. With a depth limit of about 2,000 feet, it is of moderate performance but an indication that many nations have the will and the ability to play a role in the deep seas.

6. *Deep Star III*—one of an increasing number of small submarines built entirely by private funds, in this case General Dynamics/Electric Boat, a yard that has pioneered in military-submarine design for more than half a century. This is a second-generation design with emphasis on its capability as a work boat.

7. *Deep Quest*—a second-generation craft designed by Lockheed. The hull is of an exotic steel alloy and the depth performance exceeds 8,000 feet. A lock-in lock-out chamber for divers is provided.

8. PX *15*—the *Benjamin Franklin*, Piccard-Grumman design. It is a relatively large, non-nuclear submarine built for long endurance and a large crew and has many innovations (for submarines) in the life support system.

9. DOWB—a General Motors entry. Small, deep-diving (6,500 feet), work-rather than research-oriented, this has unusual viewing optics.

10. DSRV (Deep Submergence Rescue Vehicle)—the first "production" submarine. Being built by the U.S. Navy to provide superior rescue capability for military submarines in trouble; and to double when available as a survey, exploration, and research craft.

11. *Le Redoubtable,* prototype of the submarine by which France hopes to establish a creditable ocean-based nuclear threat. In cost and tonnage, one nuclear attack submarine of the type being built by the score in Russia and the United States, and in smaller numbers by other countries, outweighs all the research and work submarines (excluding the nuclear NR *1*) that have been built to date. However, a nuclear military submarine must be self-sufficient for months. Were the cost and tonnage of the support ships required by the nonmilitary submarines also thrown into the balance, the comparison would be less overpowering.

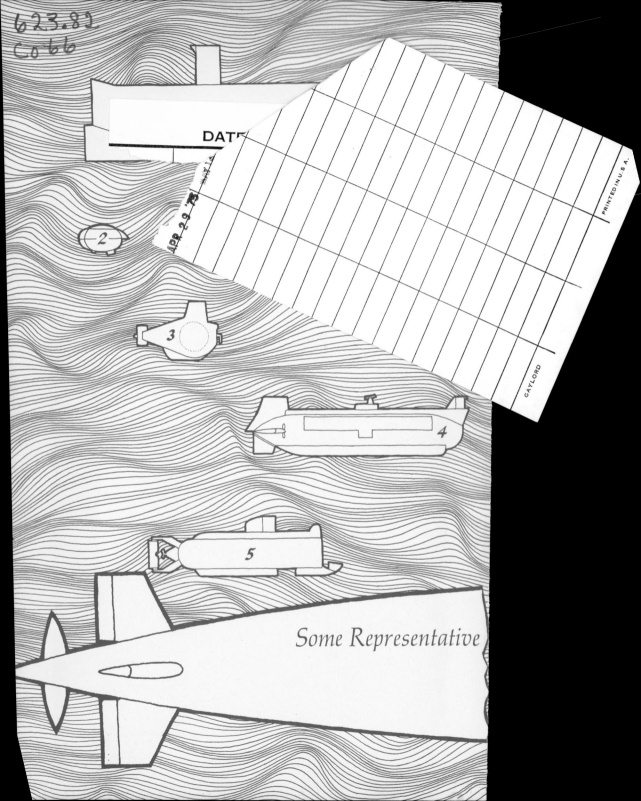

Some Representative